Ireland's Own

The 2016 Anthology
of Winning
Irish Short Stories

THREE SISTERS PRESS

The *Ireland's Own* 2016 Anthology of Winning Short Stories

Editor: Phil Murphy

Production Editor: Helen Ashdown

Design: Rosbui Media, Gusserane, Co. Wexford

Published by: Three Sisters Press Ltd. Co. Wexford

Printed by: Swiftprint Solutions Ltd. Rathnew, Co. Wicklow

Distribution by: Gill Distribution, Hume Avenue, Park West, Dublin 12

© Copyright 2016, Ireland's Own, Channing House, Rowe Street, Wexford

ISBN: 978-0-9573162-8-7

Disclaimer:

While best efforts have been used in preparing this book, the author and publisher make no representations or warranties of any kind and assume no liabilities of any kind with respect to the accuracy or complete-ness of the contents and specifically disclaim any implied warranties of merchantability or fitness of use for a particular purpose. Neither the author nor the publisher shall be held liable or responsible to any person or entity with respect to any loss or incidental or consequential damages caused, or alleged to have been caused, directly or indirectly, by the information contained herein.

Introduction

I RELAND'S OWN in conjunction with publishers, Three Sisters Press, is very pleased to bring to readers our 7th anthology of the winners and other highly commended entries in the long-running annual writing competitions organised by the magazine. This book is compiled from the 500 plus entries we received for our 2015 competitions and we are satisfied that the content is once again of a very high standard, indicative of the great writing talent out there.

Ireland's Own receives a great many submissions from our regular contributors every year, and we also receive a large number of unsolicited contributions every week. We are only able to use a small portion of all these, but we do try to be encouraging and sympathetic in our approach as we are conscious of the great desire among people to get their work into print, and the small number of potential outlets available to them.

The anthology and our writing competitions are an essential part of that policy of encouragement and support. We thank former *Ireland's Own* editors, Gerry Breen, Margaret Galvin and Phil Murphy, for their continued involvement with this worthwhile project.

We wish all contributors future success in your writing ambitions. *Ireland's Own* is very happy to have helped you along that road.

The short stories and memoirs in this publication offer a good flavour of what is available every week in *Ireland's Own*, the publishing phenomenon that has continued without a break since 1902. Our unique mix of entertaining, educational and informative features, song words, jokes, cookery, lifestyle and health, history and personal memoirs, also includes our old friends such as Cassidy, Miss Flanagan and Dan Conway, and a substantial section specially for younger readers.

Even after 114 years the old maxim about *Ireland's Own* is as true as ever, The Week Wouldn't Be The Same Without It! And for many people it is now becoming just as true that the year would not be the same without the *Ireland's Own* anthology of short stories and memoirs.

Sean Nolan and Shea Tomkins
Editors, *Ireland's Own*

Contacting *Ireland's Own*
You can check out *Ireland's Own*, sample what we have to offer, take out subscriptions and air your views on our lively website at *www.irelandsown.ie*.

Phone us at 053 91 40140. If dialling from overseas the number to ring is 00353 5391 40140.

Email articles to be considered for publication to: *submissions@ irelandsown.ie*

For general enquiries, email: *info@irelandsown.ie*.

For subscriptions: *iosubs@irelandsown.ie*

You may write to us at *Ireland's Own*, Channing House,
Rowe Street, Wexford, Ireland.

Editor's Note

A S A FORMER editor of *Ireland's Own* I am delighted to maintain my association with the magazine, having been asked to continue on as compiler and editor of the yearly anthologies.

I congratulate all those who appear in this year's production; quite a few regulars are again included, but 50 per cent are being published in a book for the first time and I am sure it is a special thrill for them.

I thank you all for your help and co-operation and I hope you feel pleased and happy with the end result.

Well done also to the hundreds of others who entered; perhaps your turn will come in next year's anthology.

A special word of thanks to Michael Harding, author, actor and philosopher, for providing a foreword for this year's edition; his support and encouragement is greatly appreciated by us, and also by all the writers.

My thanks to Helen Ashdown for production editing, Rosbui Media for design and layout, Dawn Tyrrell for proof-reading and Michael Freeman of Three Sisters Press, publishers of this edition of the *Ireland's Own Anthology of Winning Short Stories*.

My thanks also to friends and former colleagues, *Ireland's Own* editors, Sean Nolan and Shea Tomkins, for their ongoing help and support.

Phil Murphy
September 2016

Foreword

By Michael Harding
Playwright, novelist, columnist and philosopher

I AM DELIGHTED to be involved with the *Ireland's Own* annual Anthology. This is a collection of memory and story from all across the country, and contains stories by some people who have published before and some who are entirely new to publishing, and who are seeing their work in print for the first time.

In my own experience there is nothing richer than memory. When we live through an experience it is sometimes happy and enjoyable, or sometimes unpleasant and difficult. That's the mix of life. We are born and experience childhood, we go to school, we fall in love, and sometimes we marry and have children. As we get older we attend more funerals. We see more and more of our old friends, our childhood sweethearts and even old rivals pass away.

And we all come from small places, small communities, whether it is a village, a city street, a housing estate, or a townland in some remote wilderness. But we always remember the things we did as children, the places we loved and the games we played and the people who loved us.

Even if we travel to far-off cities we will never forget our home; never stop looking out the window and remembering the past.

Life is rich with blessings, and bleak with terrible sorrows, and in our memories the days that were, continue to live forever. The great South American writer, Garcia Marquez, says in his memoir that people relish life more in memories than in the actual experience.

In life things happen to us and we suffer and endure them without being able to control anything. But when we sit by the fire and remember the past, we are taking control. We are reliving the experience, not with terror but with pleasure. That's called storytelling. We can enjoy again not just pleasant things like marriages and childbirth, but even things that seemed at the time to be disasters. War, death, illness or the loss of wealth, become transformed in storytelling and we live again with a strange joy remembering the past.

Storytelling is something we do when we are grieving, or when we are full of joy. The widow describes how her beloved died, over and over again at the wake. She is remembering. The lovers leaning towards each other on the pillow tell each other where they came from, and how they grew up and what their parents were like.

It is all storytelling. And it is what makes us human.

Ireland's Own has been celebrating and encouraging the art of storytelling for over a century, and it is with great pleasure that I pen these few words for their latest anthology.

Michael Harding,
August, 2016

Michael Harding's plays include *Strawboys, Una Pooka, Misogynist, Hubert Murray's Widow, Sour Grapes,* and *Amazing Grace,* all produced by the Abbey Theatre, and more than a dozen other plays for leading Irish companies. He has written three novels, *Priest, The Trouble With Sarah Gullion,* and *Bird In The Snow.* His latest book, *Talking to Strangers,* was published in October 2016. His memoir, *Staring At Lakes,* was published in 2013. He is a regular columnist with *The Irish Times.* He is a member of Aosdána.

Contents

Competition Winners

Highly Commended

Itch of the Heart

By Richard Lysaght

Back in Dublin forty-five years after leaving for America, Don had an urge to look up a woman he had known in the old days before emigrating, but he seems to have run into a dead end and he returns to Boston in the morning …

RELIEF TINGED with disappointment ran through me, as I stood at the bar in the "Chimes" pub; relief that the woman sitting in the far corner gazing out the window on a wet, windy November afternoon, most definitely wasn't Bella. I had heard Bella was living on the streets and was to be found in the "Chimes" pub of a Thursday afternoon. At least the person who told me had the good sense to say it was only a rumour. No one had seen Bella in years, and the woman I was now looking at definitely wasn't her.

My memory of Bella was of a buxom girl with long chestnut coloured hair, a faint bloom of red on rounded cheeks and a sparkle in her eyes, which held both the colour and appeal of chocolate. The woman sitting in the corner, wearing a green coat with grimy sleeves, was no more than a loose arrangement of bones. She had steel-grey hair, cut short, cavernous cheeks covered with dirty red blotches, and protruding mud-coloured eyes that held the glint and suspicious cunning of a rat.

And even taking into consideration that it was all of forty-five years, if not longer, since I last laid eyes on Bella, there was no way that my imagination would stretch to believe the woman sitting in the corner was ever her.

A feeling of disappointment swelled in my heart: I now knew there was no chance of me finding Bella, not when I was returning home to Boston in the morning. A deep sigh of despair passed my lips, for despite the yawning gap of time since our last meeting, a part of me still treasured the memory of how special she had been to me: first love of my life, first woman to make my heart sing to bursting.

'What ye looking at mister?' A voice, with a definite snarl in it, coming from the corner, made me wince.

'Sorry, didn't mean to stare. I'm looking for a woman I used to know, was told that she might be … doesn't matter.'

'Well, if you want to show how sorry you are, why don't you buy me a drink?' she said and broke into a laugh, which was punctuated by the sound of ripping cardboard coming from her chest.

'A glass of Guinness?'

'Nothing wrong with your eyes, I'll say that for ye, and a small Paddy. Helps with clearing the ould bronchials,' she said, and coughed in case I needed convincing.

I called the barman. 'Why don't you have a drink yourself and come and sit down and tell me about this woman you're looking for. Me name's Susan, but you can call me Sue, like in the Johnny Cash song, since you're buying me drink.'

Hearing her name was Susan dispelled any notions, no matter how slight, that she was Bella, as Bella's real name was Bernadette. I looked at Sue, and though I felt like a thirsty hen being invited to sup with a fox, I called for another glass of Guinness and sat opposite her.

'What's this woman called that you're looking for; wouldn't be Gerty Malone, Molly Malone's sister, would it?' she said and laughed.

'No,' I said, taking a deep breath, 'her name happens to be Bella.'

'Bella? She from one of them places out foreign?'

'No, she's from County Cork. Worked in the G.P.O at one time. Used to go dancing in Father Brown's over by Harold's Cross many years ago. You know of it?'

'Don't like going over to the south side of the city,' Sue said, 'always stay on this side of the Liffey.'

'Well, that's where we all went dancing of a Saturday night, and everyone wanted to dance with Bella. She had long chestnut coloured hair, big brown eyes and a smile that would melt the heart of a snowman,' I said, the memory of her bringing a smile to my face.

The barman came with the drinks.

'And her name was Bella?'

'No Bernadette, Bernadette Winters, but we called her Bella because it is the Italian for beautiful and it really suited her, I can tell you.'

'Ye men are all the same, always losing what sense that's in yer heads over bauble and frippery. Ye all fall for the painted lady, don't ye?' she said, and polished off the whiskey in one gulp. She then started on the glass of Guinness.

'No, No,' I said, ' I'll be honest with you, Bella was special; her beauty wasn't just skin deep, no it ran right through to her core. She was the most kind, genuine, good-humoured, tender-hearted person you could hope to meet. Always …'

'Probably tender-headed as well, and for my money, I bet she ended up getting into trouble over it.'

'What do you mean?' I said, taking a mouthful of Guinness to push back the annoyance Sue's words were evoking in me.

Sue finished off her Guinness and stared at me, waiting.

I waved to the barman for another round of drinks for her, and a smile sparkled in her eyes, which for the briefest of moments made me see Bella. Strange how the mind tries to delude itself, but then the eyes dulled, and Bella vanished.

'Well,' Sue said, 'your tender-headed Bella probably let herself be sweet-talked and swept away by Mister Charming. And then when age attacked her beauty, as it does, Mister Charming went sweeping somewhere else,' Sue said, and laughed, till the ripping sound in her chest made her stop.

'I certainly hope that didn't happen to her.'

'You can hope all you like,' Sue said and treated the second whiskey in the manner of the first. 'Ye men find someone decent, ye abuse them, each and every time, and that's a fact, mister.'

'Not all men,' I said, in defence of my species.

'No, only the ones that are six-foot underground or under six-months old.'

'I don't believe that,' I said, knowing that I was wasting my breath, there was going to be no winning with this woman.

Sue shook her head and got to work on the glass of Guinness, while I gazed out the window watching people pass, their shoulders hunched against the driving rain, and as I did a strange feeling of sadness clawed at my heart. Could what Sue said have happened to Bella?

'If this woman was so special to you, how come you didn't marry her?' Sue said, in a sneering voice, breaking my mood.

I couldn't help but smile.

'Marry her? I never even asked her out on a date; didn't have the courage.'

'Pshaw, what ailed you?'

'Well, for one thing, I didn't have the money. I was up from the country trying to get work as a builder's labourer, and work at that time was about as plentiful as the proverbial hens' teeth. I used to have to depend on Bella giving me the odd hand out, bless the sweet woman's heart.'

'So, you were a user, like all men?'

'No, I was not.' I said a little louder than I intended and was treated to a concerned glance from the barman.

I cleared my throat and took a deep breath, while part of me inside was beginning to question if I wasn't totally mad buying drink for someone who was hell bent on abusing me.

'I always paid back what I owed; I would never have done that, not to Bella.' I said in a voice lower in tone but stronger in force.

'Leave the skin on my nose, would you, it's my only redeeming feature,' Sue said.

'Anyway, I don't think she ever looked on me romantically; I wasn't the easiest to look at, had terrible acne and…'

'You're not the easiest to look at now, either,' Sue said, 'not that I'm exactly a popular tourist attraction myself.' She laughed and then said, 'still if you were any sort of a man, you would have chanced your arm.' She tapped the empty whisky glass on the table.

I sighed. What had I gotten myself into? I signalled to the barman, determined that this was the last drink Sue was going to get from me.

'Well, I intended to chance my arm, as you call it, as soon as I went to America. I had got an invite from a relative with the promise of work, and my intention was when I got settled there to write to Bella and ask her to come over. I was going to pay her fare.'

'But you never did pay her fare.' Sue said, and made a grumbling sound in her chest and then said, 'I'll bet you didn't even bother to write to her being the typical man; all grand ideas and high notions filled with nothing but hot air and yesterday's promises.'

I took another deep breath and let it out slowly.

'I did write to her,' I said struggling to keep the annoyance out of my voice. 'I wrote to her after I had been in America for a month or so, but the letter I wrote came back. Bella had suddenly upped and gone to England and left no forwarding address.' I waited, expecting a smart reply, but this time Sue just lifted the glass of whiskey to her lips, and, keeping it there for a few seconds, tipped it down her throat. I noticed that her hand wobbled as she placed the glass down on the table.

It was time for me to leave. 'Best be making tracks.' I stood, and Sue gazed up at me and said in a slightly slurred voice, 'Why you looking for her, anyways?'

'Old time's sake. She's always been …' I struggled to find the words.

'An itch of your heart, you can't scratch.'

'Yes, something like that,' I said, nodding.

'Well, mister, all I can say is that this Stella, Bella, whatever her name is, lost out on a rare jewel in you.'

I looked at the crumpled figure of the woman in front of me and for some reason felt an immense sense of gratitude. 'Thank you for saying that.' I said, and reaching into my pocket took out a twenty Euro note and shoved it into her right hand.

'Thank you, Donal,' she said in a voice barely above a whisper.

I was at the door of the pub before it dawned on me that I hadn't told Sue my name and that no one ever called me anything other than Don, except Bella. And then another thought struck me like a thunderbolt, as I remembered Bella's middle name was Susan.

I turned with the intention of confronting her but something stopped me. Maybe it was the tears streaming down her face, or maybe it was the thought that I would be doing her a very great unkindness, the last thing I would ever want to do. The woman she once was, Bella, was now forever lost to the past. Perhaps the kindest thing I could do, out of respect for that woman who once was, would be to leave her there.

I took one last look at the woman sitting in the corner and then turning up the collar of my overcoat, took the memory of Bella with me out into the cold, wind-driven November rain.

Richard Lysaght, overall winner, is from Walkinstown in Dublin. He has appeared regularly in our winners' list since the first Ireland's Own Anthology of Winning Short Stories *was published in 2010.*

Sidesaddle

By Patricia Foran

*Marion helps her mother in their corner shop and
observes the comings and goings of the customers, but
she has a particular fascination with everything about
the stylish Mrs Sutton …*

'HERE COMES Mrs. Sutton, the lady of leisure,' my mother tells me. Mrs. Sutton's arrival at the shop usually puts my mother in bad humour; not me though. 'What'll I get for Joe's dinner tonight?' my mother mimics Mrs. Sutton's voice. 'Would you have a nice little pork chop Mrs. Kelly?'

I look out through the window, just in time to see the motor scooter turn in between the two gateless pillars. The Suttons' arrival is one of my favourite things to watch.

Mr. and Mrs. Sutton don't live very far away, but they never walk to our shop. He has a limp and he always wears what my father calls a soft hat, even on the scooter. Sometimes when I go outside after they've left, I try to walk like him, but I don't get it right.

The gleaming scooter comes closer. You could eat your dinner off it. That's what my Granny always says about Mrs. Doyle's floor. The seats on the scooter are triangle-shaped, covered in black leather, and they're wide and soft looking, not like the saddle on a pushbike.

Sitting sidesaddle, her ankles crossed, Mrs. Sutton is a lady. As Joe gently brings the scooter to a stop, she floats to the ground, touching down gently on her small, perfect feet. She looks happy as usual and gives me a little wave through the window. I wave back, my hand held where I hope my mother can't see. The smell of lavender comes in the door with her.

7

As the two women greet each other, I stand to the side behind the counter, watching Mrs. Sutton. Her small white teeth gleam behind her pink lipstick as she speaks. A white chiffon scarf protects her neatly permed, blonde hair; a pale blue cardigan is draped over her shoulders, one fastened button holding it in place over her white blouse. She is beautiful. She knows how to be perfect every day. I want to be like her when I grow up.

'Hello Mrs. Kelly. Lovely day, isn't it?'

'Yes lovely. And how are you keeping Mrs. Sutton?'

'Very well, thank you. Joe hasn't been well this week. Just a little cold I think, but he's not too bad today.'

'Well, he's on the mend then. And what can I get for you?'

'Let me see. It's hard to know what to cook sometimes, isn't it? Maybe a nice little pork chop. Let's have a look at what you've got today Mrs. Kelly.'

My mother's dark, wraparound apron passes me as she goes to the fridge.

It puzzles me that Mrs. Sutton never buys a pork chop for herself. Maybe she doesn't eat dinner. Maybe gentle Joe gives her some of his. Maybe he gives her the bone of his chop when he's finished with it. Daddy always gives his to my younger sister, so she can chew on it. I like the bones of chops.

Mrs. Sutton moves gracefully around the shop. She peeps in through the glass-topped tins of biscuits, then turns and smiles at me.

'May I have a bag Marion please?'

Delighted that she remembers my name, I pass her a paper bag.

'Which ones are your favourites?' she asks.

'Coconut Creams. I like Bourbon Creams too.'

'My favourites are Chocolate Goldgrain,' she says, opening one of the glass lids. I can smell the chocolate as she puts the biscuits in the bag. She places the bag on the counter while she examines the pork chops my mother is showing to her. Her fingernails are painted pink.

As she pays for her shopping from her red leather purse, I'm wishing she needed more things, just to keep her here a little longer. Waving goodbye, she steps lightly out the door. Joe takes the shopping bag and places it at his feet as he sits on the scooter. Mrs. Sutton leans on his shoulder as she settles herself on her seat and I watch them until the scooter disappears from sight.

'Lovely day how are you!' comes my mother's voice. 'Isn't it well for her, with nothing to worry about but what to buy Joe for his dinner? And here am I, tormented. Tormented! Why wasn't I wise like her, instead of being scourged with children?'

Torment. My teacher Miss Mahon tells us in Catechism class that if we go to hell, we'll suffer eternal pain and torment. My mother is tormented. I'm sure that Mrs. Sutton is not. I'm also sure that I'd be very happy if she was my mother. She'd always be kind and happy. Joe would take care of her and she would take care of her children. No, her only child. I wouldn't be a torment to her. I'd help her make Joe's dinner. There's even a spot on the scooter in front of Joe's knees where a child could stand while he drove gently along.

I'm still daydreaming about Mrs. Sutton that evening, as I sit with my brother and sisters watching Lassie on the spotty, black and white television screen. We hear a cry from the kitchen.

'Jesus, Mary and Joseph, have you no noses? Could none of you smell that pot boiling over? You heard the bell! You knew I had to go out to the shop. When I think of Mrs. Sutton today with not a care in the world! Isn't she a lucky woman, with no children to scourge her?'

This week, my brother is showing me how to deliver the evening papers on our road. He's going to take over the second, longer route from one of our older sisters. Peter is always bossing me and showing off. I hate him. I want to be like him. When I learned to ride the three-wheeler bike really fast, he could already ride the two-wheeler. When I climbed the tree with the big hollow in it, he showed off by climbing a taller one.

'If we're short of Heralds, the Byrnes will take a Press, but never give the Doyles a Press.'

'If you haven't enough papers, make sure Mrs. O'Shea gets one and skip Whelans.'

'Don't walk on Mrs. Russell's grass.'

'Shut Power's gate tight'

'Billy Johnson's dog Ranger is vicious. If you see Mr. Johnson on his way home from work, he'll take the paper. Or else, stand at the gate until Mrs. Johnson hears Ranger barking and comes out for it.'

I'm relieved to see that Ranger is tied and can't get past the gate.

We deliver to most of the semi-detached cottages on the road. They all look the same except for the colours of their doors and gates. Everyone knows that Mrs. O'Meara paints her gate a different colour every year.

I learn how to fold each paper so that it slides through the letterbox without tearing. Some letterboxes open easily, but others catch my fingers. At one house, I get an awful fright when someone inside the door snatches the paper as I'm shoving it through.

We reach the last cottage, but Peter has an extra paper.

'Is that one left over?' I ask him.

'No, it's for Sutton's, you dummy,' he says.

Excitement bubbles in my tummy. We're going in through that gate.

The Sutton's live in the watchman's house at a local builder's plant. The house is hidden behind a high block wall at one end of the plant. There's a wooden door in the wall that's like the door to The Secret Garden. My friend Frances and I tried to look under it a few times, but we could only see a bit of the gravel path on the other side.

As Peter opens the gate, everything slows down, like in my dreams. Short green grass on either side of the gravel path; a fairytale timber cabin, sunlight sprinkling on it through the silver birch, showing sparkling white lace curtains on the windows. A side door with no letterbox, so we walk around the house to the front door. This is where she lives.

I skip home, hands black from newspaper print, knowing I'm going to visit that house again and again.

Every day except Sundays now, I go through The Magical Gateway, as I've decided to call it. Sometimes I even get to see Mrs. Sutton in the garden and she asks things like how I am and if I like delivering papers and what class I'm in at school. One day, she even comes to the door in a white half-apron and gives me one of the fairy cakes she's baked.

On those days, I smile as I make my way home, climbing walls with semi-circular capping, jumping down at gateways and up onto the next wall. Wallflowers and pink carnations below me in gardens where there are no children. Hurley sticks, abandoned 'go-carts', hoola hoops and well chewed dog's bones in others.

On an afternoon towards the end of summer, I sneak into the store room at the back of the shop. There are lots of tempting things on the shelves. Bottles of red and white lemonade, macaroon bars, jars of bullseye sweets; but I'm there to attack the large block of cooking chocolate. As I kneel on the floor, slowly, quietly, peeling back the wrapper, my mother and old Mrs. Nolan are talking quietly at one end of the shop.

I don't like Mrs. Nolan. As far as I can see, she has only two bottom teeth and her silver moustache is horrible. When she talks to me I can't stop staring at the purple mole on her top lip, even though I don't want to look at it.

I don't like Mr. Nolan either. He always watches me as I walk in the gate with their paper. He thinks I can't see him because he stands a little bit away from the window. Sometimes, when I'm just passing the window, he opens it with a smile that's not nice. He takes the paper from me without saying anything and he has no shirt on.

'And did no-one see them leaving?' I hear my mother ask.

'Not a sinner,' Mrs. Nolan answers. 'Left like thieves in the night, after his wife appeared at the door. I heard it was one of the priests in Kilburn who helped her to find them. Jimmy Kehoe is already in for his job I believe.'

I turn back to the block of chocolate and break a piece off, then creep outside to enjoy it. My favourite hiding place is the shed in the backyard. I sit on an overturned orange crate, pulling my short dress down carefully underneath me so I don't get any splinters.

As I eat, four dead eyes watch from just above my head. Two rabbits shot last night by my father, hanging now to be prepared later. I hate when my mother sends me to the river to dump the rabbit guts. The same river which brings us kids running to admire its ever changing colours. We drape ourselves over the wall on the bridge, the vivid blues, greens, yellows, reds and oranges of the water entrancing us. The colours change regularly, along with the colours of the dyes used by the local paper mill.

I stare at the bullet holes in the rabbits. I remember that once I pulled the trigger of my father's rifle. Before going out for a night's shooting, he stood it in a corner of the kitchen, behind his chair. I remember my mother's cry of 'No' as I placed my curious finger on the trigger. The noise was sudden and terrifying.

Mostly I remember the fright, but I think I remember crying. My father joked as he hugged me. He said I'd shot a hole in the bath upstairs. My mother didn't speak. Her lips squeezed tightly together, making bumps in her chin, like when Grandad died. She didn't answer my father when he said anything to her that evening.

Chocolate eaten, I stand up, just as blood drips from one of the rabbits onto the newspaper-covered floor.

While I'm at the shop counter that evening, sorting out the papers, my mother checks on me as usual.

'You don't need to deliver to Sutton's anymore.'

'Why?'

'They're gone. Now just do what you're told.'

As I walk from house to house, I wonder how they managed to move everything. I see her clearly, sitting sidesaddle, trying to hold on to all she owns.

Patricia Foran, Beginners Short Story category winner, is from Firhouse in Dublin. This is her first time to be published in the Ireland's Own Anthology of Winning Short Stories.

Small Business 1959

By Liam Cahalan

Two young entrepreneurs-in-the-making seize the chance of making some cash by harvesting specimens for the Group Cert science students.

I SAT ON THE WALL next to the road, waiting for Tom O'Meara. The June afternoon sun was warm on my back, dappled through the leaves of big elm trees at the back of the house. Birds twittered and swooped round the thatch. Rover lay beside me, shaggy head in my lap.

I checked the equipment again, lined up beside me on the broad capping of the wall. I had the big blackened kettle, borrowed from my mother for the evening, a galvanised bucket and half a dozen Maguire & Patterson red match boxes, complete with air holes, all empty.

I heard Tom coming before I saw him. There was eleven of the O'Meara's, and the bicycles they shared came in for a deal of hard work. This one had a buckled back wheel, and it squealed on every revolution. A little older and taller than me at fifteen, red haired and freckled, Tom was my best mate. He dismounted, wheeled the old bike into the yard and propped it against the wall.

'We'll walk from here. I'm sick of that auld yoke, anyway. Where are we going?'

'We'll try the callow near the river. The cattle are out there all the year. As well as that, t'will be handy for the water. Come on, Rover.'

I handed him the kettle, picked up the bucket and put the match boxes into my pockets.

'How many boxes have you?'

13

'I could only get four,' Tom replied.

'I have six. If we can fill ten, that will be half a crown each.'

The three of us went through the gate into Deegan's garden, crossed the field, up the stile by the bridge, and crossing the far road, went into the callow.

'I'll get a bucket of water,' I said. 'You have a look for places'.

The Ballifinboy river formed one of the boundaries of our hundred odd acres, was clear and clean and teemed with wild brown trout. I fished in it as often as possible. That evening, with more pressing business in hand, I just filled up the bucket at the slip and hurried back to where Tom was crouched, intent. I took the lid off the kettle, and filled it up to the top.

'Look here, that looks like a good one.' Tom was hunkered down by an old, dried out cow dung, pointing at a round hole, about the size (appropriately enough) of a sixpence.

Taking the match boxes out of my pocket, I handed him one. He knew what to do, sliding the box open about halfway and holding it firmly, open side down. I picked up the kettle. We got into position, on our knees, one at each side of the cow dung.

'Ready?'

He nodded, intent, tense, poised with matchbox ready. I poured a steady stream of water into the hole until it just overflowed. We waited, barely breathing. Rover picked up the tension in the air, padded over and shoved his black inquisitive nose between us.

'There!'

The big shiny black dung beetle came floating out of the hole, pincers waving furiously. About as big as a bumble bee, its black double-jointed carapace gleamed as it regained its six feet and scurried for cover. Tom deftly pushed the open side of the matchbox over the escaping insect and slid the box shut.

We broke into a brief dance of triumph, shouting. Rover barked excitedly.

'One down, nine more to go. Yahoo!'

On we went, as the sun slid slowly westward. A dozen times more we formed our tableau, two skinny teenage boys and one black and

14

white and tan collie, crouched among curious cattle, intent on ancient cowpats and their precious contents.

Get into position, pour the water, wait, wait, sometimes in vain, but by the time it was too dark to identify likely locations, eight of our Maguire and Patterson boxes contained an angry occupant.

We left the callow by the gate to the Borrisokane road and walked towards my house in the twilight, bats flitting about us in the warm evening air.

Tom was excited. 'We have four bob's worth here, guaranteed. We could try for Daddies and leatherjackets and the white butterflies as well. We could make ten bob each!'

I wasn't so sure. 'The Group Cert is on in two weeks. The lads need the insects before then to mount them in the presentation boxes in time for the exam. Anyway, the Daddy Longlegs are easy to get, they're all over the place. We could dig for leatherjackets, though.'

'OK, we'll do that tomorrow.'

Tom rode away home on his squeaking bike into the darkness, four of the precious matchboxes tucked safely in his pocket.

I put the bucket and kettle in the dairy, carefully concealed my four captives, went into the kitchen and closed the door.

Liam Cahalan, overall Memoirs category winner, is from Clonlara, Co. Clare. This is his first time to be published in the Ireland's Own Anthology of Winning Short Stories.

A Bit of Bother

By Martin Malone

*Charlie was suddenly starting to feel his age; he
had woken up to his own mortality and it was a
bit of a shock to the system. A bit of luck can
bring its own responsibilities …*

HE WALKED as though something was broken inside of
him. As though the sum of years on the hurling field had
belatedly decided to exact its toll and call the dues in all at
once. For Charlie Dunny, a barrel of a man, was up until a week ago
the picture of health, a picture that often lent people in the village
into asking themselves, sometimes each other, what ingredient was
making Charlie a better looking sight than men of half his age?

Gnarled knuckles, a painful little finger, the other would never
straighten, floaters across his eyes, a constant ringing noise in his right
ear, a legacy from a slap of a hurling stick during a training session...
he had for years put up with their hauntings, but now, ah now...

He had woken up to his own mortality, and for some this realisation
grows over a long telling of time, and maybe these are the ones who
can handle the change better. Sudden awareness, like a fog rolling
in off the sea on a clear summer's night, could be a shock enough to
stop a man's heart.

He wore green cords a charity shop would reject and a drab brown
jacket, a blue scarf wrapped around his long neck. Each leg seemed
to be in worse condition than the other, a give in each knee, a slight
going down, like a coil being compressed. It was not just the knees
that told a story, for the winces of pain had become a permanent

16

feature. His hauntings, he had come to understand, were no longer silent, and were visible to all.

'You're not yourself,' Maisie Reagan said gently, joining him at the bus stop.

'Maisie,' he said, looking down on her (and not just from a position of height). He thought she was quicker than Google to spread news and reminded himself to let nothing slip. She was thin and short, a compact little woman with glasses that magnified her green eyes, revealing the intensity in them as much as it enhanced their colour.

'I'm going to the hospital,' she said, peering along the road. The bus had yet to appear.

'Yourself?' she said, turning to look at him.

'Ah, here and there,' he replied evenly.

'Is your car banjaxed?'

'No.'

'You're giving it a rest, then?'

'A rest, right.'

'Jay, if I had a car it'd be giving me a rest – walking up that bleddy hill has me nearly kilt.'

'You're looking well, Maisie.'

'You think?'

He wondered why it was that some people considered it an insult to be told they were looking healthy.

'You're not looking the best,' she said. Aired more in hope that he would confirm this and give her a morsel of fact to add with rumour she had lately gotten wind of, that all was not good with Charlie.

'Here's the bus,' he said.

He let her on ahead of him, an act of manners and cuteness, for he could sit in a seat away from her. If he were to get ahead of her, she would jump in beside him and try to rifle things from his mouth.

It began to rain as he walked toward the post office. Charlie hadn't slept for a week. He was bothered to an extreme. Not having much money didn't unduly bother him. Having 25,000 euros did. He wondered if the secret caused him to feel sore all over. Since scratching the card he'd been out of sorts, anxious, worried, and it was a huge effort to rein in his galloping thoughts.

He'd prayed for ages for a little money to come his way, enough to allow him bring Sheila on holiday. Rome was in her head – she was drawn to visiting there the way people were to places they had read about or seen on TV.

He was a quiet man; liked an evening pint, a read of an evening newspaper. Routine he loved, the cycle of familiarity, the reassurance that day follows night. He had contentment. Used to, and now? His son and his wife were about to lose their home because of extravagance on both of their parts – foreign holidays, two cars, a large house.

When Benny had told him that they owed 60,000 euros to the bank, another fortune to the credit union, he genuinely got a shock. He felt it surge through his veins – he and Sheila had always been prudent. Anger had burned a hole in his heart – how could they have been so stupid, so bloody naïve? Perhaps this had been the trigger for his being unwell?

Money woes – it wasn't entirely the young couple's fault. Other people in charge of things, responsible for the country's soundness, had given weak governance – the irony of it not lost on him – it was they who were suffering the least in the recession.

Vindictiveness was not in his nature and bitterness he thought a root a person needed to weed from their soul at first sighting, because it destroyed the carrier. And life was too short to let something you could do nothing about steal from your time.

The post office manager gave him cash, though she was reluctant, stating that it wasn't a good idea to be walking around with a stash of money on his person. He said it wouldn't be delaying in his hand, and that he wanted the satisfaction of seeing it across the counter of a certain bank – to a man he had made an appointment to see.

You think you're flying in the sky when you win a sum of money, but there's always a something to put lead in your wings, he thought. He could not bear to think of that money resting in his bank account, while his son and daughter-in-law were near to spilling tears of blood. What sort of man would allow that to happen?

He spotted Maisie ahead of him on the street. 'About turn,' he said to himself, but the bank – she was standing outside it, by the railing, haunting her face with a cigarette. He didn't know she smoked – he'd never seen a cigarette in her mouth. And she also looked pale. He'd seen that blanched look often enough throughout his life, even in the mirror a couple of times. Not a good colour for a face to be wearing. He approached her.

'Maisie,' he said.

'Charlie.'

She coughed, glanced up at the busy street. Across the road, a murder of crows nested on the ridge of a slated roof.

'Are you all right?' he said.

'Do I not look all right?'

'No.'

'I'm fine.'

'I'll be out in a second, if you...'

'Lodging your money, are you?'

'Pardon?'

'I'm joking, Charlie, go on.'

He felt he just couldn't.

'Maisie, the next bus isn't due for an hour...do you want to sit down in that cafe there, for a bit of lunch.'

'Ah you're sound, Charlie; I couldn't, but thank you.'

He grew embarrassed, felt a heat rage up his neck. He loosened his scarf. Maisie's cheeks and voice had taken on a tremor, so touched was she by his offer.

'My treat,' he said.

'Do I look that hungry and what would your Sheila say? She can be a jealous woman; don't I know, didn't I go to school with her. A gas woman, she is.'

'She'd think worse of me if I were to leave a neighbour outside on a cold day, while I was lorrying soup into myself, and looking out at her.'

19

'Is it only soup you're having?'

He smiled, 'An shure, maybe I can stretch the pocket to dinner.'

'How do you know?' she asked.

'Know?' he said. He indicated for her to enter the cafe ahead of him.

'About my results.'

He was mystified then recalled her saying she was going to the hospital. 'I...' he shrugged, 'don't.'

'I broke down outside the clinic and that Nancy one saw me – she was in a car and I got out of there before she came along; I'd have blabbered the whole lot of me – within an hour the whole town would know that my goose was cooked.'

He let linger what she had said, reading the distress in her.

'Sorry,' she said, her voice in a quiver.

He saw her brokenness. 'That bad?' he asked.

'Will we order?'

She spoke a lot, on the rise of her nervousness, about funny things that people said and did, about her grown children living abroad, how she missed them, her late husband, how the loneliness of her house seemed to have a physical presence, it weighed so much. He listened, picked at his chicken curry, while she simply studied hers – she was hungry and yet was not.

'You never said about your car?' she said, after she had run out of things to say.

The wind made a noise outside, a sudden rise, silence. 'I gave it to Benny – he needs it for work.'

'Gave it?'

'Well, lent it to him permanently.'

'Weren't you very good to do that.'

'I'll get a banger for the shopping and stuff.'

'My God, you're a good man – I'd heard you were mean...what's the word.'

'Mean, me?'

'No. Frugal, that's it, frugal.' Her expression was that of a librarian searching for a title rarely ever borrowed.

'Wise with money,' he said. 'I was, am.'

'Yes,' she smiled, 'frugal.'

'I...'

'We used to call you Frugal Charlie. I'd forgotten – it was a joke with the residents' association ...'

Of which he had been chairperson for a couple of years. He'd always tried to avoid signing off on cheques for work projects he thought could be done by the residents themselves.

He smiled.

They had coffees in front of them now, and two buses had left the stop, and it looked like he wouldn't make the bank before closing time. He would bid her stay here until his return, and he still had time yet to cross the road and do his dealings. He felt she should not be left alone.

'So,' he said, not finding it easy to knit words together.

'I'm going to see my girls, that's my plan, before I get too sick to travel,' she said.

In Australia, he knew, where her three daughters had settled.

'Have you been there before?' he said, thinking she had, but also thinking he might be mistaking her travel for someone else's.

She shook her head. 'I've been saving.'

He took a long sip from his coffee and then told her he had a secret too. Could she keep it, if he told her.

'I would of course,' she said.

'And I need a favour from you if I tell you.'

'That's odd ... but okay.'

'Promise?'

'I promise,' she said.

They sat together on an evening bus, in a sleepy sort of peace. His hurts and aches had greatly eased, perhaps because his heart felt light. Maisie had strongly resisted his offer to pay for her trip, but it was done within minutes of leaving the cafe. Solid dates for her to plan around, a little by way of pocket money.

He'd also booked a holiday for Rome. He'd made the bank too, and parted with most of the rest of his winnings – it would ease the pressure on Benny and his wife. 'You see,' he'd told the bank manager, who had been on about investments, 'we forget that none of us is guaranteed his next breath. And helping others has been a tonic. I haven't got a bit of bother to my name. Have you?'

Charlie rebuked the stony look with a broad smile. Still the hard look. 'Put it down to a little victory for the small man,' Charlie said. 'We don't win many. Not nearly enough.'

Martin Malone is from Athy, Co. Kildare. He has been a regular prize-winner in the Ireland's Own Anthology of Winning Short Stories *from the start. He is now an established novelist.*

I Cannot Convict Him – He Is Fit To Travel The World

By Eileen Caplice

Recalling a young American cousin who came from the streets of New York to a farm in Co. Cork in the 1920s in an effort to curb his unruly nature

'I CANNOT convict him – he is fit to travel the world.' This was the summing up of a juvenile court judge in New York when a twelve-year-old boy was brought before him charged with truancy and vagrancy. The N.Y. Times carried the story on its cover page the following day.

The year was 1926. The boy's name was Robert (Bob) Walshe. His parents had emigrated from Kilworth in Co. Cork in the early 1900s and settled in New York. Bob was their only child. When he came before the courts he had been missing for several weeks and was found by police selling newspapers on the streets of New York.

It was acknowledged that Bob was a brilliant child with an innate wisdom far beyond his years, as attested to by the judge who questioned him at length but could not 'catch him out'. He was returned to his parents without charge and duly sent back to school. They worried what he might do next.

Following communication and collusion which developed between Bob's father and uncle, Patrick A. Walshe, on the home farm back in Ireland, Bob was to be sent over to be educated in boarding school.

23

Between terms he would live with his uncle, aunt and ten cousins. He'd hardly be noticed.

His Aunt Ellen (P. A.'s wife) was never consulted. She was the typical saint of an Irish mother and in this case, effectively, a single parent of ten (now eleven) children because his uncle, known to all as P. A., was not only a gentleman farmer but was involved in so many activities he was seldom at home.

He was a butter buyer for The Firkin Crane in Cork, an insurance agent with the Royal Liver Friendly Society, an agent for Alfa-Laval milk separators (a high-tech piece of dairy machinery invented by a Danish company), Vice-President of 'The Lost Co-Op' in Fermoy (a predecessor of Mitchelstown, Ballyclough and Golden Vale) and a staunch member of The Order of Knights of St. Columbanus. He was also a Peace Commissioner.

His ten children, with their ten dogs, had free rein in their father's absence and welcomed their American cousin with open arms. Bob was a novelty with his strange accent and whimsical ways, his presence adding to the existing pandemonium around the farm. He had a taste for new adventure and downright devilment.

Aunt Ellen could not wait for September and the start of the school year. Bob and his cousin, Tom (later Fr. Tom Walshe, P.P. of Bristol), the youngest of her brood, were sent off to boarding school at Mount Melleray Abbey, Co. Waterford. By Christmas Bob had taken first place in his class, including first place in Irish, a subject he had not previously studied.

In January 1928, after the Christmas holidays, Bob and Tom were back in 'Melleray' and Bob was bored. The two absconded and returned home to Kilworth by shank's mare, a distance of over twenty miles. A short shrift and they were in Melleray again 'under observation'. Bob wasn't having it though, so next time he made good his escape, solo, unbeknownst to Tom.

The search began. His uncle and aunt, with all their other cares, had this additional worry. The only consolation was that he was streetwise and with a lot of experience under his belt he might be alright, but he was still only fourteen years old.

After months of searching by family and police, Bob was located in Co. Longford with the Anew McMaster Intimate Shakespearian Company which McMaster had founded in 1925. His American accent had given him away. McMaster did not want to part with Bob and fought to hold on to him. He gave glowing accounts of his brilliance as an actor; learning long passages from Shakespeare came easy to him. It seems that he had a photographic memory, a great asset for retaining reams of script.

It all came to an abrupt end when he was shipped back to America to the great relief of Aunt Ellen and Uncle P. A., wearing the same tag as he had on arrival: 'OUT OF CONTROL'. His cousins, of course, did not want him to go.

Anew McMaster and his players would have been accommodated in warm and comfortable local hostelries when performing their plays in village and town halls around the country. But before Bob caught up with them his health would have been compromised by sleeping rough in haybarns and damp ditches without proper food or dry clothing. Four years later, at the age of eighteen years, he died in New York.

His life was bright but brief, like a falling star. May he rest in peace.

Eileen Caplice is from Mallow, Co. Cork. P.A. and Ellen Walshe of Kilally, Kilworth, Cork, were her paternal grandparents. This is her second time to be published in the Ireland's Own Anthology of Winning Short Stories.

The Screenwriter

By Stephen Duignan

*Tom had emigrated from Dublin and was making his way as a
screenwriter in Hollywood but contact with home had been allowed
to drift as time went on. Now bad news is bringing him home and
he has a talkative and excited companion on the flight …*

'SO MY SON heading for a vacation or home?' The robust
woman sitting next to Tom was clearly American –
although she almost certainly would dispute the absence
of a hyphenated 'Irish' before that description. Her bursting waist-
line had encroached on the mythical barrier between economy class
seating on the aeroplane, but her weight was matched by a feverish
excitement that was usually exclusive to children on Christmas morning.

Tom had noted it from the moment she bounded through the aisle;
her carry-on was emblazoned with a 'Kiss Me I'm Irish' patch, while
a copy of Froomer's Guide to Ireland was pouched between the side
of her bosom, an inflated neck pillow and her arm. She had greeted
every seated passenger she passed on her way with a warming grin
and a 'howdy y'all'.

Initially, Tom had hoped for the same greeting – and the same
passing – as everyone else had got. But naturally, the destined path
of the last few days would not allow such a karmic moment to budge
its way past him down the air aisle.

During take-off, Tom had expected the conventional woman to
exhibit the same nervous tendencies that even some of the most
experienced flyers sometimes shed. Instead, she clapped; an applause
for a trip that was so very clearly a long time in the making. Tom

estimated that they were somewhere over Greenland by the time she couldn't stand the dull buzz of the jets outside and broke the droning static.

'Home actually' Tom replied. The response she had visibly being hoping for, journeying to Ireland, beside an Irishman. Her glinted eyes lit up behind the veiled screen of a thick prescription.

'Oh my! Am I a lucky lady! Y'know, this is my first trip, but I like to think I'm going home too. Where are you from? Near Kerry?'

'No, just Dublin I'm afraid'. Tom had no idea why he added the apology; especially after the woman's level of exuberance escalated even further with his response.

'Oh Dublin! It really is my lucky day,' the woman blurted. She raised her chubby hand to him. 'Name's Betty Clarke.'

Tom resigned any hope of ending the exchange quickly, and committed. 'Tom. Tom McCready.'

Over the next hour or so, Betty Clarke made honest work of the occasion she now found herself in. She quizzed Tom over the sights and sounds of Dublin; the museums, galleries and buildings. When Tom couldn't offer an answer, she didn't show disappointment or confusion. She simply brushed the unanswered questions to one side and went back to the well.

When they had verbally toured the deepest corners of the capital's cultural landscape, Betty pushed the boat further – first Kildare and Glendalough, then across the country to Kerry and Skellig Michael. Any details Tom remembered from his Junior Cert history seemed to be sufficient information. Betty only wanted to whet her insatiable appetite with such descriptions - the main course was only a few hours away after all.

When Tom's schooling failed him, Betty flashed another smile and powered through to her next subject. By the time an air hostess was able to flash a teasing grin at Tom and take their meal orders, Betty Clarke had reached the main feature of her questioning - pubs.

'I've made a pact to myself – to find the best pint of Guinness in Ireland; any suggestions?' Betty asked, taking a sip of her fresh coffee.

Tom forgot himself for a moment, letting out a quick snort of laughter. 'Good luck'.

For the first time during the course of their meeting, Betty seemed taken aback. Her usual enthusiasm had been knocked, and Tom immediately regretted the cynical response.

'I mean, if you find it, let me know. Most places worth their salt in Ireland should serve a good Guinness'.

Good. Why had he said 'good'? By this point, Tom knew that the phrase 'A Trip of a Lifetime' was no hyperbole for Betty Clarke. Chances are, she had saved for this moment her entire life. Who was he to brush aside any hope she had for this venture? His mother had taught him better than that. If she was there, Tom could only imagine her response. He quickly held his half empty plastic cup of coffee aloft. 'Here's to your quest Betty – may you enjoy many good pints on your journey to the best'. Her eyes quickly reignited, and her hand flew to her own cup to meet his gesture. 'Hear, Hear!'

Thomas MacCready and Betty Clarke talked all the way from Newfoundland to Iceland. Or, rather, Betty Clarke talked at Tom. She told him of her children; her son who was a senior accountant at one of the oldest firms in New York; her daughter who lived in Chicago with her husband and two perfect children. She told him how her son recently set up Skype on her computer so that she can see those perfect children grow.

It made Tom realise how little he had used the same technology to see his own family. For thirteen years, he had traded the damp air of Dublin for a chance to bask in the sun-kissed illumination of Laguna Beach and the canvas-white of the Hollywood sign. More than anything, he traded his home for a chance to be paid to write for a living, to write movies.

At first, Tom thought like many of his generation who sought chance and fortune far from the home shores that denied such things; the few hours' time difference would mean little with a laptop and a fast internet connection. He could even tune in to his nephew's communion and watch him open the card he would send.

28

Over the first few days and nights he would time his runs from the studio office to his apartment around the video call home, even conference calling multiple members of the MacCready clan and friends at once. But sure enough, life has a way of making those moments appear dispensable.

The studio brought forward deadlines and shooting schedules and before Tom could even let the ink dry on a piece of dialogue, the promise of a life and career often dreamt about soon grounded to an exiling experience. He would still text, and his mother would call sporadically to offer updates on his father's condition, but all communication traffic had quickly become one-way.

Somewhere above the Atlantic Ocean, despite his best efforts, Betty Clarke figured Tom out. The in-flight dining experience had left much to be desired, but Betty had filled Tom to the brim with chocolate and doughnut holes that she had packed in her carry-on.

Betty had performed a sort of sugar-coated interrogation. She had squeezed Tom for every ounce of geographic and social knowledge of his homeland he held. Spent, he was working his way through a handful of powdered treats and the airline's filter blend when she changed their conversation's trajectory for turbulence.

'It's your father, isn't it sweetie?' she said. The words cut through the beehive hum of the engines in flight and hung in echo. Her eyes watched him take the words in. They were the eyes of a mother; blankets of warmth in waiting. Tom hadn't told any of his friends back in HollyWeird about his trip home to bury his father, making Betty the first to point out the elephant on the airline. At first, the question brought an ease to his shoulders, as if it had released some of the pressure that had steadily built up behind his eyes since he talked to his mother the previous morning.

'How did you guess?' he asked.

She rested her head to one side, a smile of pity broke amongst the wrinkles and cheeks of her round face. 'No guessing about it my boy. My own son was just like you when my Henry passed'.

'I'm sorry Betty' he replied. Instinct had kicked in, and his mother would have clipped his ear if he had reacted in any other way. Would she do the same at her own husband's funeral? For the first time, Tom thought of his mother alone.

'He passed yesterday. I had to leave as soon as I heard, to make it in time for everything. We hadn't spoken in a while,' he said. Tom had no idea why he was suddenly spouting out things he should have probably cleared with a therapist first, but there was something about Betty that seemed safe. She was genuine.

'Oh darling, I am truly sorry to hear that…and you so far from home'. Her eyes watched him as her hand covered his on the arm rest.

'I'm sorry; I shouldn't be telling you this. I'm sure it's the last thing you want to hear on your way to Ireland.'

'Don't be. We had thirty-seven wonderful years together, and he gave me three beautiful children'. Betty wore the type of glasses that magnified her eyes, and Tom could see the deep green in them hold back a tear or something else.

'We were the lucky few, Thomas. To be given all that time together…to live. You have to believe that'. He wondered if the call for faith was really for him. Betty suddenly let out a laugh; a light chuckle to herself that Tom just knew would have been an asset in her youth. He wondered how she had looked at his age, how she had met Henry. So comfortable had he become in this stranger's warm presence, he urged himself to ask her about it.

She broke away and fumbled at her well-worn copy of 'Traveller's Guide to the Emerald Isle', holding it over the neutral zone between their seats. 'So tell me' she asked. 'Where's the best place to hear real Irish music?'

After 8 hours and 4,000 miles, Tom MacCready had realised that Betty Clarke had had enough of swimming in past waters that she was clearly still treading. Maybe she was Irish after all.

Out the plane window, past the plane's wing, Tom saw the sunrise chasing them. For the past two hours, Betty had rested her eyes and drifted in and out of sleep. Tom had no such luck; their unexpected exchange had seen to that. Mrs. Betty Clarke, the Irish-American mother, had seen to that.

Instead, he tried to busy himself and avoid the inevitable. He brushed through the in-flight entertainment, taking note of all the film and TV productions for which he had either done re-writes or scripted entirely. He counted twelve, but only three he was willing to admit. The bouncy air hostess had somehow maintained her verve since take-off, and had dropped off fresh coffee an hour ago, flashing the same warm smile she had practised on Tom during the safety instructions. This time, he smiled back. The captain's voice came over the intercom to rouse the passengers that had been successful in getting some sleep.

'Good morning ladies and gentlemen, this is the Captain speaking. We are just about to start our descent into Dublin, where the weather on the ground is a brisk 13 degrees. We would like to take this opportunity to thank you for flying with us. Céad míle fáilte.'

Betty rose to the few Irish words with the smile of a woman well rested. She blinked herself awake and smiled before re-greeting her new travelling companion. 'Good morning my boy. Did you manage to get any sleep?' she asked.

'Afraid not, but I'm good.' Tom replied.

Betty didn't reply at first. Instead, she pulled her large frame over his chair as far as the now compulsory seatbelt allowed her to and gazed out the window. The plane had descended enough for the coastline to come into view, pale blue ocean cut against jagged stone and green fields dotted with brief signs of life. Roads cut across like lines drawn in ink. The catching light of the morning set it all to a lighter shade.

Betty smiled and looked at Tom. 'You will be son. You will be'.

Stephen Duignan is from Malahide, Co. Dublin. This is his first time to be published in the Ireland's Own Anthology of Winning Short Stories.

.

In My Granny's

By Bernadette Melia

The scent of a box hedge triggers memories of many years earlier and another box hedge that led the way up to granny's door and all the happy visits that were made there during childhood and later.

I CARRY MY wicker breakfast tray out onto the sheltered, flower-filled patio. As I devour a chocolate croissant, a silky breeze envelopes me in the heady scent of the nearby box hedge. Another shift of sultry air settles around me and I'm wafted back in time to another cherished garden.

Box hedge lines the crunchy gravel drive that slopes up to my Granny's moss-green doorway. Sparkling beneath the hedge, 'snow-in-summer' cascades, lacing itself over large, white-washed stones. Tucked under the drainpipe leading from the roof, the rain barrel stands brim full. An enamel basin of creamy blancmange sits outside on her kitchen window sill. Alongside it, brown bread covered in a damp, linen cloth cools in the country air.

I spot her white-haired bob at the window, her solid frame wrapped up in her fuchsia-print apron. She glances up at the slow crush of tyres on the loose stones. Dad lifts the latch and we crowd into her pristine scullery. In a quiet corner, crab-apple jelly plops rhythmically through a muslin sieve.

Seconds later, sitting by the kitchen window, we slurp chicken soup from orange, marble-swirled bowls. I watch dreamily as the hens in the yard outside enjoy a feathery, flip-floppy dance around each other. My brothers eye up the forbidden territory in the top field. Countless haystacks are piled up begging to be bounced on. Uncle

Jack's grey donkey peers in the window at us with a knowing glint in his eye.

Next to the warmth of the kitchen is the inner sanctum of my Great-Granny's bedroom (or Grandmother Olc's room as my cheeky uncle nicknamed it). The sound of her soft snoring escapes from under the woolly blankets.

Born in Gaelic-speaking south Kerry, she couldn't bear the electric light to be turned on in her room nor to see the flash of a camera – but photographed she was (at least once) propped up in bed with her pale blue shawl draped around her vulnerable frame.

Across the stillness of the geranium-laden hallway, the Clancy Brothers, the Wolfe Tones and the Johnstons bellow intermittently from the record-player in my uncle's room, breaking the Sunday morning serenity.

Upstairs, a perfect peace reigns. I put my head around the door of the small, spare bedroom that will be mine for a whole treasured week of my summer holidays. Kneeling on the patchwork bedcover, I gaze out the window. Across the fields, strong mares with spindly foals close by their sides shimmer in the veil of early mist that still hangs over Eyrefield Stud. I can't wait to get hot toast with lashings of butter on it served up to me in this feather bed.

Then, I sneak into her huge bedroom. A dusky rose-embellished jug and basin sit in her washstand below the lace-curtained window. A shaft of lemon sunlight spills onto the bare floorboards, sparkles across her glass-topped dressing-table, sprinkles itself over her blue-and-gold bottle of 4-7-11 and explodes onto a vase of lavender-blue hydrangeas.

Who gave her this lovely perfume? 'Echt kölnisch wasser … like champagne on my skin' - or so it says on the telly! I dance her papièr-machê sailor doll across the shiny glass. Where did Granny get this fancy fellow from, in his navy velvet suit?

I peep into her makeshift jewellery box with its inscription of "Cogadh na Saoirse" embossed in gold on its outer lid. I finger her white pearls, rolling their smooth shapes round and round. I try on her diamond engagement ring that never sees the light of day.

Nestling into the softness of the crocheted cover on her bed, I engross myself in the latest book from her bamboo bedside locker. She calls up to me. 'Coming,' I say as I play for time. She calls again.

'On my way.'

'Ah! Sure, so is Christmas!' Her heavy footsteps recede and I skip downstairs swirling in a cloud of 4-7-11.

Later in the afternoon, I hear her searching for the "comrade" of a sock. Comrade? My young ears perk up. How come my Kerry Granny pronounces that strange word with an English accent? Then I come to a mesmerised halt.

I spot a transformed tomato crate in the alcove under the stairs. Using remnants of material, she has quilted the wooden crate with a kaleidoscope of patchwork – crafting it with her clever hands into the most beautiful doll's cradle. She has hand-stitched matching bedcovers for it. And not only that, but she has made a new pink dress.

After getting a roasting from her for ransacking her precious haystacks and to get into her good books again my brothers collect the newly-laid eggs for tea-time. They deliver a dozen en route to Mrs Wilson, Granny's neighbour, through the secret gate in the picket fence between their two back yards.

The lads make this delicate delivery at high speed. They're fully convinced that Mrs Wilson is secretly a witch – all because she dresses in black, has a waist-length, silvery braid and a large mole on her left cheek that sprouts hairs from it. But I like her. She has chocolaty-brown, twinkly eyes.

My eldest brother is checking if the coast is clear. What's he up to? Before I know it, he's whizzing out the door of the log shed on Granny's black Hercules bike. Small stones fly like silver sparks from the spokes, but not half as fast as the hens do. He ducks his head down and pedals for all he's worth past the kitchen window, slithering down the driveway towards the lane and the ever-beckoning river. He keeps his fishing rods buried in the ditch down there.

I bet he'll stop off at O'Brien's sweet shop on his way. He'll throw her bike under its poky window and gallop in. And there they'll be in all their glory – jelly beans, rubbery wine gums and black-and-white bulls' eyes, all gleaming out of tall glass jars in the half-dark of this Aladdin's cave with its low ceiling, sparse shelving and grim walls. The old man will be there as always, staring from behind the steel scales that sit with bated breath on the pock-marked counter.

Granny will have his sacred life when she catches him after he gets home with her bike. "Hercules" had made its maiden voyage all the way up to Kildare from Kerry in the back of her brother's Morris Minor in the 1920s. She often talks well into the night about how she used to race around Caherciveen on it as a young nurse. So, taking Hercules is nearly a hanging offence.

From underneath the archway in the box hedge Mam emerges into the back yard with baskets full of lettuce, rhubarb and gooseberries. Dad fills the bucket from the water pump outside the gate but not before I perch myself on the pump's freezing, looped handle. It creaks laboriously up and down.

Back indoors, my sister smothers fresh bread with crab-apple jelly. A sliver of sun dips behind what's left of the haystacks as we pile in the door like a herd of hungry calves. A tractor seems to have ploughed across the evening sky leaving fluffy pink clouds trailing behind in its startling tracks.

After tea, a few old neighbours meander in and take their time-honoured places around the wide hearth where a few summer embers of turf linger. Granny shows us all off. They "ooh" and "aah" as though they had never set eyes on us in their lives before. Sure aren't we there nearly every Sunday?

Having updated each other on all the hair-raising events that occurred since 11 o'clock Mass in Kilcullen earlier that day, they drop gingerly to their bony knees on the unforgiving stone floor. Leaning their wrinkly elbows on the seats of the rickety chairs, they begin the rosary.

It flows gently and naturally out of the ends of their conversation. It's hard to figure out where one begins and the other ends. On cue, my brothers start tittering one by one just because they know they can't. My giggly sister joins in. So do her blonde ringlets. Within seconds, the whole lot of them are falling out into the yard doubled over. Granny will go for them in a big way later on.

Big Mrs Murphy decides that she needs to use the white-washed outdoor privy, so they all peep through the cracks in the wooden door at her. They'll give us a low-down on the colour of her drawers the whole way home in the car across the Curragh Plains.

Last week, it was old Bill Dunne's sad, grey long-johns that they spotted trailing out from under the jagged end of the panelled door while he enjoyed the Sunday Press on his bleached pine throne. The week before that, we got a running commentary about Mrs Wilson's English niece who was seen sporting not the common-or-garden variety of watery-blue knickers that you can buy ten-a-penny around here – but black frilly ones!

And if they're not describing everyone's bloomers, they'll be snorting about the rough toilet tissue that's more like army-issue greaseproof paper. My youngest brother's party-piece is to press his angelic curls against the door's rough grain, squash his freckly nose up against it and plant his cherub lips to the keyhole chanting 'You liar, you liar - your pants are on fire! Then he scarpers for cover into the hen-run.

Driving homewards later on, moths tap gently against the windscreen in the humid air as we pass under Eyrefield Stud's lacy canopy of beech trees. Past its gateway where Dad's childhood dog used to wait – faithfully and in vain – for my Granddad's return from work. Past the seductive sweetshop tucked away in the hedges near the crossroads. Past the "cabbage for sale" sign and the huge, silvery milk churns that sit crookedly on the roadside table outside Jameson's farm.

The morning sun catches Granny's ring in its searching rays. It sparkles on my finger as I start on my second croissant. Shortly before she died, I'd cycled out to visit her in the nursing home. Safely wrapped inside a linen tea-cloth in the basket of my bike was a half-dozen of my warm scones. She had taken me into the orchard garden to sit with her in the crisp, autumn air – placing her black handbag between us on the white, wrought-iron seat.

Rummaging through it, she came across blue, wafer-thin airmail letters from Australia, her bottle of 4-7-11 and her prayer book with its yellowing, dog-eared bundle of memory cards. Photos of family and friends long gone peeped out from its Sacred Heart cover.

This time, it wasn't the usual long bars of Cadbury's Milk Chocolate in their purple wrappers that she plucked out of her bag's unfathomable depths. No - this time it was a minute, navy box rimmed in partially-worn gold. I recognised it instantly. She popped the tiny metal button on the front of the box to open it and there, cushioned in deep velvet, sat her pretty engagement ring. Without a word, she closed the box carefully and pressed it into the palm of my stunned, nineteen-year-old hand.

Under an ancient oak tree on the home stretch, I stopped to shelter. I took another peep at her exquisite ring. Like captured raindrops in the leaves of a lupin, diamonds glistened from the depths of the dark little box. I hopped back onto the saddle and whizzed homewards through the puddles.

Our fluffy black cat springs onto my lap as I stretch out on the sun-lounger. I sink back deeply into the chair's cosy folds, close my eyes and whisper a prayer.

Bernadette Melia is from Newbridge, Co. Kildare. This is her first appearance in the Ireland's Own *Anthology of Winning Short Stories.*

My Father's Flock

By Nora Brennan

*'It wasn't until my mother fed a spoon of whiskey to the lamb that
I saw signs of life; it shook in response to the sharp bite …'.*

THEY CAME in their innocence heralding the arrival of spring. The new lambs, with faces that would melt snow, were my favourite animals. We had lots of them in the fields and we often kept about four or five pets around the yard. Pets usually came about when a sheep had three or four lambs but could only feed two. Then my mother would step in and rear the extras.

One cold frosty March evening in the late fifties my father came in from the fields at dusk carrying a new-born lamb by the forelegs. Its head was slung on one shoulder and it looked dead.

'She had three fine lambs but will only feed two,' he said, with the animal dangling by his side. 'I'm not sure if this one will survive.'

My mother went for the bottle of whiskey and I cleared the fireplace of chairs and clutter. A few sheets of newspaper were spread out on the floor and the lamb placed near the warmth of the fire. Certain it was dead, I still prayed and turned the bellows to ensure a good fire. I desperately wanted to have a pet.

It wasn't until my mother fed a spoon of whiskey to the lamb that I saw signs of life. It shook in response to the sharp bite. She then scalded a glass bottle and teat and warmed milk in a saucepan on the two-ringed table-top cooker. A seasoned teat feeder, when the milk was ready and the slumping lamb held on her covered knees, she prised open its mouth and fed it, much of the milk flowing down its crinkled skin. But still the lamb swallowed and its eyes were taking in the new surroundings.

'He has enough for now,' my father said, 'we'll feed him a sup later on.'

He went out to prepare a bed of hay in The Potato House while we tried to stand the lamb on the floor. I wanted to keep it in the kitchen all night and not put it out in the cold.

'He'll be grand now once he has the milk,' my mother said, reassuring me. Later on in the evening my father brought the lamb back into the kitchen. Now more bright-eyed and perky, he stood on all fours and beneath him a yellow stream trickled onto the Irish Independent newspaper. He drank more milk and I could see he was already beginning to thrive.

Three other pet lambs came along that spring and, as they grew and graduated from The Potato House to the haggard, we continued to feed them milk from the cows twice a day. They grew to love us and we them. Soon it was time to wean them off milk and return them to the fold in the field. The grass in the haggard was their first introduction and sometimes I stood at the gate and held a bough of hawthorn while they picked and plucked the soft green shoots until the branch was bare. I was wont to nibble a few sweet leaves too while I waited.

Meanwhile, the field at the back of the house was speckled with sheep and lambs. Sheep lay like lumps of granite in the grass while their young gambolled around the sloping banks of ditches. When the day came for the pets to join the flock we hung around near the ditches as if to reassure them that all was well. In the evenings they would come to the gate and cry but we were not allowed to feed them. Now they had to fend for themselves.

Tailing the lambs was not a job I liked to witness. They were corralled in at the end of the lane along with the sheep. My father and older brother, both agile and swift, hooked them in one by one. With a lamb held between his legs, the head out back, my father caught the tail high up and with one sharp twist of the hands, broke it off, the lamb letting out a sharp cry.

The hardest time of all was when lambs were separated from sheep. The lambs would remain in the lower yard overnight while the sheep were put out into a nearby field. All night the sound of sheep and lambs bleating was heart-wrenching; I would lie awake and listen to their pitiful cries. The following day the lambs began a new life on their own. Days turned into weeks and we, letting them go, turned our attention to new calves and the sow that had just birthed a litter of bonhams.

Nora Brennan is from Kilkenny City. She has consistently been published in the Ireland's Own *Short Story and Memoirs categories over the years and was a prize-winner in the Memoirs category in the Ireland's Own anthologies on two occasions.*

Prodigal

By Anne Delaney

Brian Molloy from Connemara is leading a multi-faceted, high energy lifestyle as a trader on the New York Stock Exchange but lately the pressure has been getting to him more and more; suddenly a voice from the past may offer him an alternative way forward …

MONDAY MORNING on Wall Street; the opening bell of the New York Stock Exchange rang out as usual on the dot of 9.30am, signalling the start of the day's trading session. Brian Molloy had been at his station before 7.30 that morning, getting ready for the rollercoaster day ahead.

He drew a deep breath when the bell rang, conscious that his fingers were trembling. There was a time when he had looked forward to the cut and thrust of the continual auction format of the Stock Exchange but now he found himself struggling with an ache in the pit of his stomach at the start of another frantic day.

As usual he was wearing a beautifully tailored lightweight suit and handmade shoes – casual elegance was the name of the game; he knew how important image was to those who made their living in the cut-throat world of share trading in the New York Stock Exchange. A sharp brain and a driven work ethic were not enough to impress potential clients – and rivals. No! He needed to look the part, he needed to project the right image, to network successfully with the right people.

He would be lucky to arrive home at his luxurious apartment by midnight, for his was a high pressure career. His job as a trader meant huge rewards but involved huge risks. When his gambling on shares paid off, the financial rewards were enormous. But when he bet wrong his potential losses and those of his clients were mind-blowing.

Acid rose in his throat when he contemplated the serious misjudgement he had made the previous week. He surreptitiously popped an antacid tablet, hoping that none of the younger traders would notice. Few traders lasted into middle age, he knew. Today, he thought frantically, today he would show the younger traders what he was made of.

The tolling of the bell that initiated the day's trading died away. Brian had seen many eminent people ringing that bell, including Nelson Mandela and a smiling Irish Taoiseach. It was regarded as a singular honour. He glanced briefly at the podium. He had heard during the course of casual conversation that today the bell was being rung by an elderly Irish visitor, who had distinguished himself as head of an international charity and who was to be accompanied by his wife and daughter.

Brian swallowed, as he contemplated the day and the week ahead of him, forgetting about the Irish visitors. His treadmill thoughts were momentarily disrupted by the sound of Irish voices and he looked at the visitors with mild interest. From Connemara, he thought fleetingly, catching the echo of a familiar brogue. An unexpected ache filled his throat.

Summer in Connemara, he thought; maybe raining, maybe balmy, maybe both at the same time. The hills around the family farmhouse would be covered in gorse, the tangled hedgerows would hum with honey-bees and there would be spotted cows in the fields. It was so long since he had thought of his home place. For a moment he could smell the scent of the jasmine that used to drift through the air on a hot day. Then he thrust the moment of aching memory away from him and jerked his thoughts back to the stresses of the moment.

'Showtime,' he muttered under his breath.

By the time the closing bell sounded at 4pm, signalling the end of the day's trading, his head was pounding with a headache and he felt every one of his forty-five years. He rose from his seat, trying to straighten out the kinks in his back and a twenty-eight year-old fellow trader accidentally jostled him.

'Sorry, man', the young trader said jauntily. 'I'm in a hurry, didn't see you.'

'No problem,' replied Brian, smiling a little ironically and standing aside to allow his colleague pass.

He had been a young man in a hurry too, fresh from Ireland and from a bitter fight with his widower father who wanted him to stay and run the family farm in Galway. But he knew that he was made for bigger things, for bright lights, for success. He had been determined to prove himself – so determined that he missed his sister's wedding and the christenings of his three nieces.

And, as the years passed, and after the unexpected death of his father, the contact with his family at home dwindled and almost died; all that was left was the annual Christmas card with a scribbled line or two of greeting and the small annual income, derived from the leasing of the farm that he shared with his sister. He told himself it didn't matter; work filled his life, he had built a rewarding career for himself in the fastest moving city in the world. He spent his vacations in Aspen or Malibu. When the Celtic Tiger economy crashed, he congratulated himself on escaping from that financially doomed country.

He rubbed his temples as the old memories rushed in. Had he remembered to bring the migraine relieving painkillers with him this morning? There was a securities' sales manager he needed to touch base with and he needed a clear head for that. He picked up his jacket to check and then felt a light touch on his arm.

'It's Brian, isn't it?' asked a hesitant Irish voice. 'Brian Molloy? Your sister, Aoife, told me you were working here and asked me to say hello when I was visiting with my father. He rang the Stock Exchange bell this morning, you know. I was allowed to come back to have a look around. You probably don't remember me but we were at school together. You used to walk me home sometimes.'

Brian turned and found himself looking down into a vaguely familiar face, seeing a woman about five years younger than himself, with dark hair and blue eyes. He could hear the lilt of Galway in her voice, see the impact of her Irish genes in the delicate whiteness of her skin. She was smiling rather tentatively at him as if unsure of her reception.

Yet again memories flooded his mind and he was transported back to County Galway. It was a June day over thirty years ago and he was walking home from the village school with some friends when a high-pitched little girl's voice sounded behind him, calling his name.

'Brian! Brian Molloy!' the small voice had cried. 'You wait for me. I know your father told you to mind me today. My big sister can't mind me. She has spots everywhere, even on her toes. Imagine! She has to stay in bed and be quiet. And you have to bring me home and take care of me. You should carry my schoolbag too – it's too heavy for a child of my age, Mam says.'

He remembered groaning aloud, belatedly remembering his father's last minute instructions to see his small neighbour safely home.

'I have better things to do with my time, Deirdre O'Connor!' he had responded sulkily. 'You can find your own way home and you can carry your own schoolbag, too! Go away, I'm busy.'

But his curt words had fallen on deaf ears.

'I'll tell your Daddy,' had responded Deirdre shrilly. 'I'll tell him you wouldn't mind me, even though you were supposed to. He told my Mammy that you would. You're meant to hold my hand and bring me home. You'll be in terrible trouble if you don't. Your father will give out to you and it'll serve you right! So there!'

'Oh, will you see her home, Brian, for goodness sake,' interrupted his friend Seamus wearily. 'You know she'll follow us, giving out at the top of her voice, till you do. She's a great one for abiding by the rules, is young Deirdre. Just give in.'

Brian had opened his mouth to argue, then shut it again, resigning himself to the inevitable.

'What a pest,' he had muttered angrily, falling back and stretching out his hand reluctantly for her bulging schoolbag.

And so had followed two weeks of mortification. She had insisted on holding his hand all the way home while she chattered non-stop about the small events of her day. She had beamed her delight in his company, her earnest blue eyes shining with innocent hero-worship, impervious to his many rebuffs. It was a big relief to him when her older sister recovered from the measles and could relieve him of his escort duties.

He shook his head slowly, remembering.

'Deirdre O'Connor,' he said in his New York twang. 'I don't believe it – after all these years! How are you?'

She smiled and the thought crossed his mind that she was beautiful. How hadn't he seen that twenty-five years ago, before he left home?

'I'm fine. Enjoying our stay in New York, seeing all the sights and exploring the shops – but it's still good to see someone from home. And you Brian – are you well? Aoife speaks of you often, she's so proud of big brother who's carved a big career for himself in the competitive world of the New York Stock Exchange.'

He felt the smile congeal on his face.

'I don't keep in touch as well as I should, I suppose,' he said stiffly. 'Life here is so hectic and multi-faceted… And what have you been up to, Deirdre? I have a vague recollection that you got married about ten years ago. The usual husband and kids, I suppose?'

She raised a quizzical eyebrow, hearing the condescension in his voice.

'Multi-faceted…' she said musingly. 'I suppose my life is a bit one-track compared to yours… I was widowed five years ago and I have one child, a girl, and I work as the local GP in Kilcarrick. I know your three nieces pretty well, as I'm their family doctor, even though they're fit as fiddles, thanks be to goodness.'

He could feel the colour seep into his cheeks. She saw it and smiled at him, obviously amused by his assumption that nothing ever happened in his home place.

'I'm awful sorry, Deirdre,' he said awkwardly, his New York twang abruptly deserting him, slightly to his own shock. 'I didn't know that you'd been widowed, that you'd become a doctor. I didn't know.'

'How would you know?' she asked calmly. 'Don't apologise, Brian. I'll tell Aoife I met you and that you're looking well. She's been entertaining hopes for a few years now that you would come home and take over the farm, you know. She hates leasing it but it's too much for her to cope with. I'll tell her that you're now a quintessential New Yorker – with a multi-faceted, hectic life - and that she should continue to lease the land.'

She smiled kindly at him and held out her hand, preparing to go. He wondered a little dazedly when the adoring little girl he knew had been transformed into this composed woman who looked at him with such tolerant amusement. He wondered why she seemed to be the most important person in the room.

He gripped her hand so hard that she winced a little, her eyes widening.

'Deirdre! Don't go. Are you free tonight, or maybe tomorrow night? I know all the best restaurants in New York. You can tell me all the news about Kilcarrick. I would like … like to get to know you again, if I may.'

She shook her head slowly.

'Sorry, Brian. I'm tied up tonight and we're flying home tomorrow. My mother-in-law is minding my little girl for a few days while I'm in New York. I didn't want to leave her for too long, you know.'

He saw her face change and soften when she spoke of her daughter and was reminded of the earnest little girl he used to know all those years ago.

'Well then, I'll see you in Kilcarrick in a few weeks' time,' he heard himself say calmly.

She frowned at him, taken by surprise.

'Really? You're going to visit Kilcarrick at last? Your sister didn't mention that you'd be coming home this year, after all these years.'

He smiled at her, unaware that he was still holding her hand. One of his fellow traders gave him a sideways glance in passing. He didn't notice.

'Oh, yes,' he said softly. 'Yes. I'm coming home.'

Anne Delaney is from Phibsboro, Dublin. This is her first time to be published in the Ireland's Own Anthology of Winning Short Stories.

The Little Yellow God with the Green Eye

By Martin Malone

In the evenings she sat by the fireplace in a car seat a friend had given her. Out in the yard was a donkey and cart used to ferry home turf from the bog …

MY UNCLE EDDIE had some memories he wanted to share. He began by speaking about my great-grandmother, Ann Guidera, from Mountrath, who married William Kelly. William served for seven years with the British Army in India, arriving home in 1893.

Eddie spoke of staying with her during the summer holidays from school, in her little cottage in Mountrath, of her being a loving grandmother who always wore a Sacred Heart badge. In the evenings she sat by the fireplace in a car seat a friend had given her.

Out in the yard was a donkey and cart used to ferry home turf from the bog. By day, he and his brother roamed and played in the fields, and carried buckets of water from the well, a mile away, to the house.

Of his grandfather, he mentioned the poem he'd taught his mother, my grandmother, to recite: *The Little Yellow God with the Green Eye*, a poem written by Milton Hayes in 1911.

William Kelly spent a considerable number of years in the British army; apart from his service in India, he served in the Boer war and in World War I.

A figurine of the infant Jesus is among others he brought with him from India and feature every Christmas in my mother's house – 122 year-old figurines of a Christian crib and its ritual brought back from the Far East.

Eddie spoke of how the poem must have meant a lot to his mother, Maggie, my grandmother, because even in hospital on the day she died, she was able to recite a little of it. She mentioned, too, his visit to his great-grandparent's grave on the outskirts of Mountrath.

He also visited the house where she'd lived, where the fireplace Ann used sit at roared back memories to him as he sat enjoying tea and cake in a lovely extended and renovated home.

I thought about my uncle's stories and researched Milton's epic poem. It's about a soldier called Mad Carew and the colonel's daughter, both of whom loved each other very much. He wrote to her and asked what present she would like off him for her 21st birthday; she jokingly replied that nothing would do for her except the green eye from the little yellow god.

Mad Carew went and stole the emerald ... but his beloved's response was not the one for which he had hoped.

She upbraided poor Carew,
In the way that women do,
Although her eyes were strangely hot and wet,
But she would not take the stone,
And Carew was left alone
With the jewel that he'd chanced his life to get.

I picture my grandmother as a child listening to her father recount the poem, and perhaps he breathed of his adventures in India, the customs he'd witnessed – the long voyages and forced marches, tales of fakirs and snake charmers, of monkeys that stole items of his kit, of sitting atop an elephant and of tigers coming in the dead of night to the villages and snatching children from their beds, and of revenge the natives exacted upon those who dared to violate and disrespect their temples.

On a whim, I took to the road to Mountrath in February to see if I could locate the grave of my great-grandparents. I hadn't thought to ask my uncle of the whereabouts of the grave, assuming there was no need … the dangers of acting on a spur of the moment.

Two old cemeteries hang either side of the road, about three miles outside Mountrath. In the first were crops of small headstones, with details time and weather eroded. Snowdrops in full bloom covered the small hilly cemetery; baby stars with the kiss of rain on them. No joy here, though, in the search for my great-grandparents' grave.

At the gate I turned and said a couple of prayers, and asked the guardian spirit to direct me to the grave in question. Then, I crossed the road to the other cemetery. Here stood the ruins of a small church and a lone living figure. I'm sure of this: he had a 2015 registration Skoda parked outside the boundary wall! We exchanged pleasantries and after I told him what I was about he directed me to the grave.

There, I put down some flowers; ran my fingers over their inscribed names in greeting. I'm forever mindful of how time marches alongside the written word, and so whispered a recital of the first verse …

> *There's a one-eyed yellow idol to the north of Kathmandu,*
> *There's a little marble cross below the town;*
> *There's a broken-hearted woman tends the grave of Mad Carew,*
> *And the Yellow God forever gazes down.*

Martin Malone is from Athy, Co. Kildare. He is a former Irish army officer and United Nations peacekeeper. He is the only person to have two entries published in this edition of the Ireland's Own Anthology of Winning Short Stories.

The Promise

By Tina Sweeney

Jenny idolises her big sister, Sarah, and they share so much together until Sarah gets sad and has to go away. Now she is due to return home …

AS SOON AS I open my eyes, the excitement is back. It rushes up inside me like a tickly volcano and I jump out of bed with a shout of joy. Sarah is coming home today!

Sarah is my big sister. She is the best sister in the world. She was already eight years old when I was born – two years younger than I am now – and from the very start she took care of me. Mam says she used to rock me to sleep every night, and in the morning she was always there to pick up the toys I threw out of the cot.

Our house is filled with photos of us together. Sarah taught me everything as I got older. She helped me with my homework. I could always go to her whenever I had a problem. We used to share a bedroom. When I had bad dreams she would rush over to my bed and shush me back to sleep. Sarah always made everything alright.

When Sarah was sixteen, Mam cleared out the spare room and made it into a lovely new bedroom.

'Sarah's a big girl now, she needs a room of her own,' she explained to me.

Sarah left me all the dolls. She said she would come back to my room if she wanted to play with them. I visited her new bedroom. It was so different from ours. There was makeup and nail varnish on the dresser, and clothes I had never seen before in the wardrobe.

'Sarah, what about when I have a bad dream?' I asked.

'We'll both leave our doors open,' she said. 'You just call when you need me and I'll come running.'

I made her promise, and then she crossed her heart so the promise couldn't ever be broken.

* * *

'Jenny, are you up yet? They'll be here soon.'

I hear Daddy calling up the stairs. I throw on my shorts and tee-shirt and rush down, jumping the last three steps into his arms. He has to grab me to keep us both from falling.

'Jenny, you're like a hurricane!' he laughs, and for a second I see my old Daddy again, smiling and happy.

'Isn't it great, Daddy?' I blurt out. 'Now that Sarah's coming home we can all be happy again.'

As soon as the words are out I know I've done it again. Why can't I just keep my mouth shut? The laughing face is gone and 'sad Dad' is back. That's what I call him now. It seems the whole house has been sad since Sarah left.

'Yes, it is great,' he says quietly. He keeps his arm around my shoulders as we go into the kitchen. I know he wants to say something else, but it's like he can't find the words. I wish I had that problem. I find too many words too quickly. Maybe if I waited like him I'd find the right words instead of upsetting everyone.

'Jenny, Sarah's not completely better yet. You do understand that, don't you?'

'I know she's been sad, Daddy,' I say in my most grown-up voice. 'But I can make her happy again.'

The car pulls up outside. Sarah's home.

* * *

I ignore the groans of the trampoline as I jump higher and higher, stamping my feet into the canvas with each jump. If I jumped right up to the moon they'd be sorry! They'd probably be glad to get rid of me. Obviously I'm not wanted around here. All they've done all morning is tell me to be quiet and go and play. I've hardly had even a minute to talk to Sarah. And I have so much to tell her.

Mam has been fussing all over her, talking all the time, telling her stupid things like how they're building a new shopping centre across the bridge. Why would Sarah care about that? And Daddy - Daddy just sits there, saying nothing at all. What is wrong with him? What is wrong with everyone?

I thought once Sarah came home we could all be happy again, but now I wonder if we'll ever be happy again. Did Sarah's sadness infect the whole house? Like when I caught that 'flu bug in school and came home and gave it to everyone? But after a few days we all got better. Can't we all get better from the sadness too?

Sarah looks different now. Her hair is still blonde, of course, like mine, but her eyes look funny. Sleepy or something, I'm not sure. And when I hugged her I could feel her bones. I don't think she used to be that thin. Or maybe she was - it's a long time since I hugged Sarah. Not like in the old days, when she was always hugging and kissing me.

She told me once that a boy had kissed her at a Youth Club disco. She didn't tell Mam that, though, just me. She said parents don't understand those things. I'm not sure if she meant all parents or just ours. But they were all fighting a lot then – Sarah and our parents – and there were lots of doors slamming and Mam was cross all the time. Once, even Daddy got cross with Sarah.

And somehow around that time Sarah started getting sad. But nobody knew. She never said. One night she closed her bedroom door, and I wondered how she'd hear me if I had a bad dream and called her. I knew then that something was wrong. I should have told Mam. Maybe she would have realised that Sarah was sad and things wouldn't have got so bad.

* * *

It's eight o'clock and I'm lying in bed trying to sleep. Can you believe it? Sarah's first day home and they sent me to bed early. It's not even dark outside. I can still hear the kids playing on the street. I used to play with them, but one of them said mean things about Sarah, and now Mam won't let me play with them anymore.

I hear a door closing quietly and I sit up in surprise. Have they sent Sarah to bed early too? I get out of bed and tiptoe across to the door. I can't hear anything. I open it a tiny crack. I can see Sarah's door opposite, closed. I sink down onto the carpet, keeping the door slightly open.

I've spent many hours here, watching Sarah's door. I remember nights when Mam would come and tap on the door and whisper to Sarah to let her in. But Sarah wouldn't. Once she left a tray on the floor outside the door, but when she came back later it was still there. All of Sarah's favourites were on it – even chocolate biscuits – but Sarah wouldn't open the door. That night I saw Mam lean her forehead against the door and cry. I didn't know until then that parents cried too.

* * *

It's dark now and there are no voices from the street. Sarah's door is still closed. I wonder if she is asleep. I slip across the dark landing. I press my ear to the door. No sound comes from inside. Now that I've come this far, I have to see her, just to make sure she's really here, really alright.

As soon as I open the door the bedside lamp comes on. Has she been waiting for me?

'Well, come on then,' she smiles, sitting up and lifting the duvet for me to slip underneath. My feet fly across the carpet and I launch myself into the bed. I am wrapped up in a big comfy bundle of soft duvet and warm Sarah.

At last, at last, at last – Sarah's home.

Hot tears I didn't know about come bursting out from somewhere inside me. I sob as Sarah holds me until there are no tears left. Then I realise that Sarah is crying too. Not like me - noisily, childishly - but quietly, long slow tears running down her face. I reach up quickly and wipe them away.

'I'm sorry, Sarah, please don't cry. You're not sad again, are you?'

'Are you kidding?' she grins. 'This is the first normal thing that's happened since I got home!'

Suddenly we are both laughing madly. She's right. This is normal for us.

'I really missed you, Sarah,' I whisper.

'I missed you too, Jenny.'

'Why did you have to stay so long in the hospital?'

She doesn't answer straight away, and I think that she has become like Daddy, trying to find the right words.

'Jenny, do you know what happened that night?' she asks.

'I know the doctor gave you tablets to stop you being sad,' I begin. 'And Mam said you got mixed up and took too many.'

I know I should stop now, but I just can't.

'But Billy Morris said you took them on purpose. He said people do that when they want to die.' I hold my breath for her answer, but she stays silent.

'Sarah?' I whisper. 'Did you want to die?'

She closes her eyes and sighs.

'Yes, I think I did.'

'But what about me?' I wail. 'Didn't you know I needed you?'

I sit up and pull away from her.

'I'm so sorry, Jenny,' she cries, sitting up as well. 'But I guess – I guess in that moment – I just didn't think about you!'

I am so shocked that for once I am speechless. I scramble out over the duvet and huddle against the end of the bed, hugging my knees under my chin. Sarah comes after me, kneeling beside me. She takes my hand.

'I'm so sorry, Jenny,' she whispers. 'Will you forgive me?'

But I don't know if I can forgive her. *She didn't think of me.* I can't believe it. I can't understand it. I think of Sarah all the time. How could she not think of me?

I pull my hand out of hers, shaking my head, tears pouring down my face.

Sarah turns to lean against the end of the bed like me. We are silent for a while. When she speaks her voice is soft, like she is telling me a story.

'Do you remember the bad dream you used to have where you were running and running but never getting anywhere?' she asks. I nod.

'Well, it was sort of like that. Only I was climbing. I was down at the bottom of a deep, deep hole and I kept climbing and climbing but I couldn't get to the top. I felt so alone, Jenny. The hole was so dark. I just wanted it to end.'

I think about my bad dreams, and how scary it is when I'm in the middle of one. How would I feel if I couldn't make it stop, if there was no Sarah to come and comfort me? Would I want to die?

'You should have called me,' I whisper.

'What?'

'That's how I make the dreams stop,' I explain. 'I call and you come. If you had called me I would have come and saved you.'

Sarah shakes her head slowly and looks at me.

'I wish I had thought of you, Jenny. Maybe I would not have done it.'

Now she is crying those long slow tears again. All I want is to make it better. I take her hand.

'I forgive you, Sarah.'

We are hugging again, and though it is not completely better yet, I know it will be.

'Sarah, will you promise not to get sad again?'

'I can't do that, Jenny,' she sighs. 'But I do promise that I will always think of you no matter how sad I get. Cross my heart.'

'And I promise I'll always come when you call,' I assure her. 'Cross my heart.'

We smile at each other, friends again, making promises that can never be broken. Then Sarah says I should go back to bed and get some sleep.

'Better leave the door open,' she calls as I cross the room.

Now I'm smiling on the inside too as I go back to my own room, leaving both doors wide open. I know now that everything will be alright. I will take care of Sarah.

I will be the best sister in the world. I know how.

Sarah taught me.

Tina Sweeney is from Enniscorthy, Co. Wexford. She was last year's overall winner in the the Ireland's Own Anthology of Winning Short Stories.

The Visit

By Kate Carroll

He is determined to talk to Rosie and get something off his chest that has been bothering him for a long time but it is only now that he feels free to tell her ...

SATURDAY AFTERNOON arrives, the time planned to make the visit. Despite the significance of the occasion I don't feel the need to dress up, leaving on my old green slacks and Aran sweater. I brush a lump of hard turf from the front of it, the remains of my mornings work on the bog. I lock up the two dogs in the outhouse so they don't follow me and cause a distraction from the job at hand.

My mind is surprisingly peaceful as I make the short journey out the road towards my destination, waving to a few neighbours en route but choosing to not time waste or stop for idle chit chat. There are plenty of opportunities for this, today not being one of them. If I delay I might lose my resolve for the mission. Within a few minutes I have reached the row of uneven granite steps that marks the entrance.

Now I am here I am not feeling as brave as I did when planning it while lying on my bed late into the night. I walk slowly over towards where she is but stop while still a short distance away. In spite of the racing of my heart, I don't greet her with an embrace or even a handshake. Out of respect I simply remove the old tweed cap, the one I was given a few Christmases back, and stuff it into my trousers pocket.

I have planned this moment for such a long time that small talk seems unnecessary, preferring to get straight to the reason for my visit. I start by simply calling her name 'Rosie' and the soft breeze seems to catch it and carry it far out across the ocean.

I remind her of when we first met forty years ago, me a tall gangly, awkward teenage boy with my distinctive mop of jet black hair and she a couple of years my junior. She was pale skinned with freckles but it was not her looks that had been the attraction for me but her jovial personality, so different from my own.

I had been drawn to her like when the north end of a magnet meets the south end of another. It was her smile that had attracted me to her and it was her eyes that held me prisoner, those sky blue eyes that seemed to dance with life and laughter. Over the years I had observed that no matter what she had come across, nothing or no one could take the life from her eyes. Not even when life itself seemed to be leaving her body.

I take a quick glance over my left shoulder; no one is within ear shot unless the young fisherman in his boat, lifting his lobster pots in earnest expectation down the rugged cliff below could hear. I sincerely doubt it, but still lower my voice to almost a whisper; this is a private moment, not to be shared.

'Do you remember the picnic we shared in our youth?' I ask. How we laughed and chatted as we made the journey to the cove on the far side of the island on our old black bikes, hers borrowed from an older brother and hence a couple of sizes too big. While with many people I struggled to converse easily, this was not the case with Rosie. The cove was frequented more by gulls and seals than by people, partly because it could only be accessed down a steep incline, but that had added to the excitement as she gave me her warm hand and let me escort her down the cliff.

We had laughed together as we scaled the rock pools in search of some wildlife of which there was plenty as these little rock pools were rarely disturbed by excited dogs splashing through them or the invasion of a child's fishing net.

'Do you remember the crab I found and chased you with across the sand?' She had squealed in exaggerated fear. This was the first time

I had the undivided attention of someone of the opposite sex, and it made me feel manly.

As the afternoon turned to evening, tired from the cycle and a swim in the gentle waves, we had lain side by side in the clover meadow at the top of the cliff and watched the fluffy clouds overhead. In a rush of adrenaline and bravery I had plucked up the courage to kiss her. 'Did you realise this was a first for me?' I ask her gently. Unless you counted the pecks that I gave mother before climbing the stairs to bed at night or the farewell kisses that Granny extracted from me on a Sunday evening before she headed home to the mainland.

I hoped she had not noticed that I was a novice and that night as I lay in the small bedroom, shared with my identical twin brother, I couldn't sleep. I was sure the thumping of my heart in my chest would wake Jim up. After this day I had often wondered had she realized the teenage prank we had played and that it was I and not Jim she had spent the day with?

She says nothing so I keep on with my memories as I talk about the time a group of us in the foolishness of youth had taken the currach out to sea on a stormy April day. I was just so excited by the closeness of her presence that the danger of the situation didn't bother me. I was with Rosie and that was all that mattered.

However when we were greeted on the shore by a group of angry adults we all realized the stupidity of our actions and there was many a lecture given that evening in homes around the island and we were told how lucky we were that it was school we were all going to be sent to the next morning and not the graveyard at the top of the hill.

It has often been said of me that I am a man of few words and they seemed to have got even fewer with the passing of the years but on this occasion I have no problem. They flow from my lips like a little mountain stream after a rain shower on a summers day, slow and steady. In the distance a big black crow perched on the stone wall lets out a wail and causes me to jump. I look in all directions to see if it is a person who has caused the crow to talk. There is no one in sight.

I kneel down on the soft green, well watered grass in an attempt to be nearer to her and I say nothing for a few moments as I enjoy the closeness of her presence. Then, as if out of nowhere, a huge feeling of regret suddenly comes upon me, threatening to ruin this encounter like the arrival of a dark ominous cloud on a sunny day.

For a moment I am taken aback, drawn into the darkness of the emotion, and I listen to the voice in my head that tells me I should have had this conversation a long, long time ago. This has been an all too familiar voice over the years. Spurred on by a determination to not be distracted from what I have come to do, I start to talk again.

In the distance, I hear a rumbling of a cart making its slow journey up the hill; I suddenly realize I must speed up. 'I am sorry Rosie, if what I am about to disclose burdens you in any way'. I couldn't contain the intensity of my emotions any more and I just have to let her know the depth of my feelings for her in case I explode.

'Rosie, I am so sorry for never telling you before how much I love you. What stopped me, when the wedding ring, worn so proudly on your left hand had the inscription 'Burke' on the inside, my name?'

The cart is almost at the top of the hill so I quickly get to my feet. I turn around to face her for all the while my back has been to her and walk over to where she lies. I pause for a fraction of a second as I pass by to read the inscription on the newly erected headstone and then stop at the grave beside hers, that of my parents. I pull a bunch of squashed wild daisies from my pocket and place them on their grave. If questions were asked as to my reasons for being here, the flowers would give the answer.

I climb back down the cold granite steps and walk down the hill feeling surprisingly lighter. I had said it, too much, way too late, but then maybe now one chapter in my life was over I could try and start another. I nod a hello in the direction of the driver of the cart and head towards the solitude of my cottage.

I can feel the familiar unwanted guest, beginning to climb into my head and trying to engulf me, this guilt that I had waged a war with for years. The guilt of my secret, never uttered aloud until this day, that of loving my brother's wife, the reason why I could never wed another.

59

bringing it back, shaking their headscarved heads at him and looking fierce.

They would nod at each other as they went about their business. They usually brought one or other of the children to help them. Our Saturday dinner was always the same, mince balls with potatoes. After the shopping was put away, the butter was put in the big pot filled with cold water.

That pot was a multi-purpose pot as it was also the pot that was used to bring the hot water up the stairs to fill the Saturday bath. It was also the Christmas pot used to boil the puddings. It stands now on my top shelf in retirement, as it has served us well over the years and deserves its place there.

My mother would stand with floured hands, in her pinny, making the mince balls, a tear running down her face from the cut onion, gently lowering them in the spitting dripping. She turned them as they browned and then at that moment adding the bisto. If a toddler had become grisly she would hoist it up on her left hip at the same time as stirring a pot with her right hand. These mammies then knew how to multi task before the word was invented.

After the dinner was cleared away my father would ask 'Has anyone got homework to do?' Four voices would answer no at the same time. Then the baths would begin, the girls first. The water was clean then, but by the time the fifth came it had gone a bit murky. But I don't think the boys minded too much. Each of us got a little of the watered down Vosene shampoo.

While this was all going on my father would polish the shoes, while listening to the wireless. Polishing away, sometimes pausing to laugh at the Clitheroe Kid. All those shoes were highly polished and lined up in a row awaiting Sunday.

After the baths were finished, the delph put away and the shoes shined, the Sunday clothes were laid out, white socks and clean white vests which only really stayed white for the day. Then the youngest were put to bed, and the two eldest allowed to stay up for the Saturday film.

Thank God I was the eldest, I would sit in my flannelette nighty, my feet under me cosily on the sofa in anticipation of the film. Then the scullery door would be shut for the day and the lights put out. The only light was the flickering fire casting shadows on the flowered wallpaper and the flicker of the little black and white TV in the corner.

The fire guard would be put in place to protect us from sparks. With the coal glowing and hissing, breaking the silence, the film would begin. Bette Davis would look out at us, mesmerising, with such classics as ' Whatever Happened to Baby Jane'. After the film my father would make toast for our supper. This was pre-toaster days, so he used a toasting fork, made from the wire of the briquettes. Warm butter would run down your fingers from the toast which we would lick off.

All too soon Monday came along; Monday didn't seem to have any smell at all apart from porridge. Gloomy faces sat at the table worried about schoolwork not done. Mammy would look out the window for clouds, worried about the weekly wash, and go and get the big pot which she used for boiling the wash. We would all sit and sigh and wait for the next Saturday.

Margaret Hayward is from Monkstown, Co. Dublin. This is her first time to be published in the Ireland's Own Anthology of Winning Short Stories.

Disappearing Dreams

By Patrick Willis

*A family tale of mystery and intrigue, and hard times, from the 1950s
when Ma had taken to the bed and Da is struggling to cope with
the children and life …*

T HE DOUBLE BED in the front bedroom had never been designed to sleep six. It was extremely difficult to get any sleep in a three at the top, three at the bottom set-up. The snoring was not the only problem. A foot, and often a smelly one at that, in your nose did nothing to help sleep come.

It was the winter of 1953 and the icicles were hanging from the window inside our room. We all huddled together in the bed because we could afford nothing bigger or warmer. In many ways it gave us comfort as it provided us with a form of heating. We were always hungry at night as there was so little food in the house.

My da always tried his best. He would always gather us all together before he headed out for the night. He would tell us all to go off to bed and behave ourselves. He would then come up to the room to see us all and sit and tell us a ghost story. He never would tell us where he was going but we had our own ideas.

John, the eldest brother at 12, reckoned he was going out to do more hours in the sawmill, so he could get more money for us. Joseph, 11, said he thought Da was a special agent and he was going out on a secret mission. Ellen, a year younger and the elder twin girl by two minutes, agreed with her other twin, Lisa, that Da was going out hunting for fuel and food. I, having just celebrated my eighth birthday, felt my Da was a leader of the current troubles between us and the English. I had just read about the exploits of the Easter

Rising. Maisie, the youngest girl, said she didn't know where he went but she wanted him to stay at home.

My ma was a strange woman but you would have liked my da.

I could never guess his age. I thought he was about sixty. All people looked old to me. My da had receding hair and a little fine moustache. It always looked like there was a little worm crawling over his lip. He walked with a very slight limp. He had told us he had fallen out of a tree when he was young and broken his ankle and since then he had never fully recovered his normal strength in that ankle.

God knows he did not get it easy. My ma did very little to help us get out to school in the mornings. She always seemed to stay in bed. If it wasn't depression it was "one of her heads". I thought people only had one but John said he was sure she must have her other ones hidden under the bed in her room. She was a woman of little emotion and never asked us how we were or how things had gone at school. She was a small waif-like woman who never seemed to eat anything at all.

She seemed to want to hide away from the world all the time and since I could remember she had never even left the house.

Morning time in our house was a nightmare. My da and all of us got in each other's way. It was usually a case of first up, best dressed. The race to the outside toilet was like a sprint.

The door lock was always broken so once inside you had to keep your foot firmly against the door to stop someone else entering. My da never complained though. He just plodded away as best as he could. He never even complained about my ma, indeed he often just made excuses for her. He told us that she had once been a lot of fun and had done a lot when we were younger but she had become ill and never recovered fully. He had never specified what the illness was.

Da always went to his work at the sawmills on a bicycle. I used to laugh as he put on his bicycle clips, I could never understand what they were for. When I asked him, he said they were to stop little puppies climbing up his trousers legs and biting his behind. I believed him and fought long and hard with John and Joe about it.

My da always told me special stories. He knew I loved to listen to his tales. He once told me, and only me, that Mrs Monaghen next door had two talking cats. I spent hours in the garden holding conversations with them but they never spoke. When I asked da about it, he only said that was because they did not want anyone to know about their special powers.

I always liked it when the time came for him to tell us his ghost stories. The strange thing was, that no matter how frightened we were, we always wanted more. It was as though the fright was addictive. My favourite was the tale he told of how he had been coming home one foggy night from a visit to his mam. He had taken a route across fields as it was closer.

In this field there was a large stream which was crossed by a little special footbridge. According to my da, it had become foggy very quickly and he could not find the footbridge at all. Then suddenly from nowhere a light shone right onto it. He crossed over and on looking back he noticed the light was gone and once again the bridge was in darkness. The fog was so thick that it could not have been from the lights of a car on the main road. He swore that this was true and he never again used that route.

Over the next few years my ma got a lot better. She would sometimes be there in the mornings helping with breakfast and helping us out to school. In the evening she would make us all tea and ask us how we had got on at school. We all found this odd as we had got so used to her showing no interest at all.

She would organise a bath for us once every few days and on one occasion I heard her sing in the kitchen. This gave my da a bit more time for himself and he was able to organise things better. He still went out at nights and several times we had overheard my mother questioning him about where he was going. He would only ever reply that it was something he could not talk about.

Then it happened.

One morning without any warning he was not there. My ma looked distraught and said she didn't know where he was, he had not come home from the previous night. She said she could not cope with this and went back to bed without a thought for us.

We spent all day looking for him. We visited the town and asked in all the shops and pubs. Only Paddy Moore had seen him and that was about ten o'clock. Our search was in vain. It was as though he had vanished into thin air. We looked for days afterwards and still no sign. We checked the hospital and the police station; they said they had no one answering that description there.

John had to take on my da's duties. He tried to get work in the sawmills but with no luck. They had heard about my da's disappearance but they could not take someone as young as John. Finally, he got a job at McCartney's grocery store at the weekends. It didn't pay much but Mr McCartney would often give him a few things to bring home for us to eat.

Poor Ellen had to try and run the house. My ma had got more depression and her only sister, Vera, had "enough problems with her cats", without getting involved with us lot. Ellen lost lots of her education and her dreams of being a nurse disappeared.

Night after night we guessed what had happened to my da. Joseph said he had heard about aliens in America and maybe they had captured him. I reckoned he had been shot in a fierce gun battle and had been secretly buried in an unmarked grave, in a battle for Irish freedom.

John just got angry with us and told us to shut up and to not talk about it again.

We all just plodded along and we all had to grow up quickly and become men and women before we had ever experienced adolescence.

After three years, suddenly he reappeared. He refused to say where he had been or what had happened. He talked very little. Da had changed a lot. He looked even older now and his sense of fun was gone. He never asked how we were or even how ma was. He never went back to the sawmills, or indeed to any work. Every morning he took a long walk out to the cliffs. Bit by bit he seemed to give up on life.

Then one Friday evening, out of the blue, he called us all into the kitchen, ma included. He said he felt it was time we knew what had happened him three years ago. He said he had been going out for a drink that night when he was stopped by a police patrol. He didn't know any of them as they were not locals.

He said they had questioned him and accused him of being involved in the Border Campaign. My da said he had denied any wrongdoing. The police had told him to leave immediately or they would shoot him. When he had asked about us, the police had told him that they knew where he lived and if he went back they would see to us all.

He said no more. That night we talked long in bed about it all. The girls said little. Joseph said he still believed he had been to space. I was so chuffed as I felt I had been nearly right. John soon put me right. He pointed out that if what my da had said was true then the Black and Tans would have been to our house immediately. He said my da was lying and we fought for ages. I refused to believe John was right.

Next morning, Joseph ran in screaming. He had found da, hanging from a rope in the barn. I cried for ages. He had been such a hero to save us from those police and now he had to take his own life to make sure we got no more bother.

The funeral was the usual gathering of people who always came to say how sorry they were when someone died. We knew that da had been well known but we were surprised at how many people turned up that morning. Many of them were strangers to us. One woman, in particular, stayed on long after the rest had left the graveside. Soon, only her, her two children and us were left.

She approached my mother and astounded us all by saying that da had been living with her for the missing three years. In fact, he had been with her many times over the past ten years and the two children with her were theirs. According to this woman, da couldn't live with the guilt of leaving us and came home. Obviously, he couldn't live with the guilt of leaving them either.

I looked at the heaped soil on the graveside and all my beliefs and my dreams disappeared down the hole where just minutes before my da's body had been interred.

Patrick Willis is from Portadown, Co. Armagh. This is his first time to be published in the Ireland's Own Anthology of Winning Short Stories.

Fostered

By Richard Cahill

A slice of contemporary Irish life as experienced by those people often struggling on the fringes of society where a young mother fears her child will be lost to her …

TUESDAYS AND Fridays I get to see baby Sean. His foster mother, Bernie, drops him in to me. She comes at ten and collects him at one. Cath, the social worker, comes as well. I'm not trusted enough, it seems, to have him on my own. Cath takes this very seriously and never lets us out of her sight. I know she's only doing her job, but surely to God she can see how much I want to have him to myself, for a little while at least. Five minutes alone with my baby! Is that too much to ask?

This place is tiny, the only place we have since the council threw us out. Tommy's fault, of course, as Ma never tires of reminding me. She never had any time for him, said she knew the minute she first laid eyes on him he was nothing but trouble. A loser and a user, she said, and if I couldn't see that for myself, I must be blind.

Tommy was living at home then, but his father threw him out after a row one night. Ma said no way was he moving in with us, not for a single day. Between me giving her a hard time about it and Tommy buttering her up, she caved in eventually and agreed to let him sleep on the couch until he found a place of his own. But a week turned into a fortnight and a fortnight a month, until in the end he was with us nearly full time.

Oh, I was blind, alright, taken in by that big cheeky smile and those wide, blue, innocent eyes. Fell for him like a ton of bricks, I did. I knew what Ma meant about him being a user, but I didn't care. The odd joint, that's all I ever saw him use. He'd disappear sometimes, three or four days without a word, and I'd be out of me mind wondering where he was or what he was doing. But sooner or later he'd always turn up.

No explanations, mind you, only the wad of notes he'd slip down me front. I'd be mad as hell, but he'd only laugh and tell me to chill. If Ma wasn't around he'd roll a smoke and we'd pass it between us. He'd be sure to start coming on to me then, and all the times I swore while he was away that I'd never let him near me again would be forgotten. I guess that's how I got caught with little Sean.

The last time was different though. He'd been gone for the best part of a week and when he came back he was in a bad way, cuts and bruises all over and a gash on his forehead that nearly took his eye out. He wouldn't hear of going to the doctor, so Ma got hot water and disinfectant and cleaned him up as best she could. He was real quiet too, nervy and jumpy and all the time running into the front room and peering out the sides of the curtains. I tried to get him to tell me what happened, but he told me in no uncertain terms to mind me own business.

There was an awful bust-up one night a few weeks after that. Myself and Ma got thrown out of the house on account of it, even though we'd nothing to do with it. We were in bed, Tommy on the couch downstairs, when this unmerciful pounding on the front door started, and all this roaring and shouting for Tommy to come out or they'd torch the place. Next thing I heard the door being kicked in and glass shattering below in the hall. Then more shouts and curses and stuff being smashed and flung around and Tommy pleading and bawling for them to leave him alone. Some of the neighbours must have called the cops because we could hear the sirens getting closer and closer.

As suddenly as it started, it was all over and everything was quiet again apart from the screech of tyres as a car sped away up the street. I jumped out of bed and dashed down the stairs and there was Tommy, out cold on the kitchen floor, blood everywhere and the place wrecked. The cops called an ambulance, and by the time it came Ma was in such a state that I couldn't leave her, so Tommy had to go off to hospital on his own.

I haven't seen him for a while now. Tuesday is visiting day in the Joy so it clashes with my access to Sean. One of the cops told me it was drugs them heavies were after, stuff Tommy was skimming off on the quiet. He said he was a lucky man to be alive and if he'd any sense, the minute he got out of prison he'd hop on the next plane out of the country.

So here I am, stuck in this grotty little flat, waiting for Bernie to come with Sean. She'll be here any minute now and I'm as nervous as a kitten. I gave half the night thinking about him, trying to picture his little face and the funny way he scrunches up his eyes when he smiles. I kept wondering if he'll be wearing the baby-grow I bought for him. I picked it up cheap in a sale, but I thought it looked nice - blue, with a little bear on the front and a white hood. I tried to imagine his room in Bernie's house and all the fancy things I know I'll never have for him. I cried myself to sleep thinking about it.

She's lovely, Bernie is. She's had Sean since he was a few weeks old, and he's going on seven months now. Pure mad about him, she is, absolutely besotted. And as far as he's concerned, Bernie is his mother, not me. He roars his head off the minute I go near him, and screams his heart out when he sees her leaving. It takes me ages to calm him down and between that and trying not to make a fool of myself in front of Cath, it wrecks me head. I'm afraid I'll drop him, or do something stupid, another black mark against me that will push back the day I get to keep him full time even further. I'm trying so hard to make a good impression, but I'm all the time terrified I'll mess it up.

I don't know how Bernie does it, I really don't. She has two of her own, little girls, six and ten. Deep down, she must know Sean won't be with her always. She must be terrified the day will come when I'll be able to look after him myself and she'll have nothing more to do with him. All that love and care she's given him. All the nights he's

71

been fretful or sick, and she sick herself with worry – all the times she's washed and changed and fed him, all those days and weeks and months, and her love for him growing and growing. And then a day comes when she just hands him back and there's the end of it; he's gone out of her life forever. I couldn't do that, not in a million years.

Maybe I'm not cut out to be a mother at all. That's what I think sometimes when I see the love in Bernie's eyes for my little fella. She'd die for him, the very same as she'd die for one of her own. For someone else's flesh and blood! Fond as I am of Bernie, I know I couldn't find that kind of love in my heart for one of her kids. I could never love anyone else's child the way she loves mine.

Maybe they were right to take him away from me. What have I got to offer him, anyway, compared to Bernie? What kind of life would he have here, his father a jailbird and his ma in a dump like this, seven floors up, and the place crawling with scumbags and junkies? By the time he'd be starting school, he'd be like all the other kids around here, just another little hoodlum running wild. Ruined for life he'd be, only a matter of time before he ended up where his daddy is.

I don't know what's up with me this morning. Me nerves are in bits. I'd chance a smoke only I'd be afraid they'd walk in and catch me. That Cath one is no fool. If she got a whiff of that stuff around the place, it'd be down in me file in a flash. I sent Ma off to the shops to get her out of the way. I hate doing that because she adores little Sean. Why wouldn't she, and she his gran, but there isn't room here for all of us. And Ma gets so upset, angry at the way they took Sean away. She blames Cath, but Cath's not the one who decides what happens to him. I've no great love for the woman myself, but I know she's only doing her job. Ma has no hold of herself, she really hasn't. What she comes out with sometimes wouldn't look good in me file, that's for sure.

She's here! Bernie's come with little Sean! I feel such a foolish gratitude when I see him kitted out in the baby-grow I bought for him that I have to stop myself running to Bernie and hugging her. I'm so excited at seeing my baby again that at first I hardly register the fact that Cath isn't with her. She got held up on another case, Bernie is telling me, and won't be here for an hour or so. The arrangement is that she will stay with me until Cath arrives. I can see Bernie's embarrassed having to tell me this. It's lovely out, she smiles, trying to ease the awkwardness, we might take a breath of fresh air while we're waiting. Bernie's voice comes through a swirl of emotions that moves me like a zombie towards the door of the flat.

I'm ashamed of the lift, ashamed of the smell of puke and filth as we judder slowly downwards. Sean snuggles deeper into Bernie, eyeing me warily from the security of his foster mum's arms. He's getting big now and heavy to hold. I'm trying desperately to think of some where half decent we can go to sit and chat for a while.

In her early forties, Bernie is still slim and beautiful, effortlessly elegant and composed in a way I'll never be. What I feel about her is all mixed up. There is gratitude, of course, and the comfort of knowing Sean is loved and well cared for. But guilt and resentment are there too; the sense of inadequacy I feel at not being able to take care of my baby the way she does, makes me hate her sometimes. I worry that the longer he stays with Bernie, the stronger the bond between them will be. If and when I get to keep him full time, how will I make up for what will be lost to him; how is he ever going to accept me as his mum the way he now accepts Bernie?

The lift jerks to a stop. Bernie is holding Sean firmly, protectively; holding him like she might never let him go. She is making baby talk to him, running her fingers through his thatch of little dark curls. He smiles and babbles for her; in his little world right now I don't exist. I feel something break inside of me, a pain so deep and terrible that I almost cry out. But the door of the lift is sliding open, and I just follow them quietly out onto the street.

Richard Cahill is from Cahir, Co. Tipperary. This is his second successive time to be published in the Ireland's Own Anthology of Winning Short Stories.

Joe

By Vincent J. Doherty

My grandfather had little formal education and knew lots of tough work and hardship in his life, but I always thought he was the wisest and most gentle of men …

I ALWAYS THOUGHT my grandfather was the wisest of men but he was no scholar. When he was a youngster at the end of the 19th century his father, seeing no need for book learning, took him out of school to earn his own living. He was seven years old at the time and left his classroom to attend to a big farmer's horses, feeding them, mucking them out and looking after their harnesses. By the age of ten he was ploughing, a boy struggling with two greys in the stony, mountainy fields of Donegal.

I also thought him the gentlest of men and could never imagine what he must have gone through in the mud and blood of Flanders thirty years before I was born. I remember him once explaining to me as we walked the fields how he got involved in that slaughter.

'Sure we thought we were going for a month or two to see what it was like, to see the sport. We'd never been to any place beyond the town on a Fair Day before so it was like a bit of an excursion.

'But if we didn't know what it was going to be like, we soon found out when we got there. A lot of the boys from 'round here never came back and some of the ones that did, came back with an arm or a leg or their wits missing. We never talked about it to anybody. Sure who would want to know about things like that?

'Some fool said we were coming back to a land fit for heroes but when we got here there was no land fit for heroes, there was nothing but more trouble and no work. So we had to look out for work across the water. They were building hydro-electric dams in the Highlands of Scotland and whenever I heard about them I was on the Glasgow boat.

'That was hard work, navvying, and when it was over I was on the train to London. Mind you it wasn't all sweat and toil, London could be great fun. A week's work, doing jobs like building artificial rocks for the films they were making at Elstree, then a bath on a Saturday dinnertime and away on a tram to Highbury, the Arsenal, and a big picture in the evening.

'They were grand evenings. You didn't just see the pictures; they would have an organist playing as it was rising up out of the ground in front of the screen. It was like magic.'

What I knew about my grandfather I learned in fits and starts at odd moments when we were looking for gaps that might be open or carrying out the odd jobs that old men and young boys had to do about a small farm. Or we might just be looking at what was growing and how it was getting on.

He was never as satisfied as when gazing across the drills of Arran Banners, Kerr's Pinks, Gladstones or King Edwards greening away into the distance as far as he ever wanted to see. Then he would keep a deep breath, as if to take in the strong fresh smell of the dark green leaves.

He said once that after the noisy back-breaking years of sweat-soaked labour and being crammed in with too many other people in crowded lodging houses in Cricklewood or Kilburn, a man had elbow room in a place like Tullyard.

You could set your watch or your calendar by him. He always planted his first potatoes on St.Patrick's Day and dug the first of them on the Twelfth of July. Like all farmers, with however few acres, he was always on the go but there was still time to savour a certain amount of pleasure from the few flowers he grew, huddled almost apologetically at the edges of our vegetable plot. Against the hedges were the clusters of snowdrops and daffodils that he said looked forward to the coming spring in the last biting days of winter.

I learnt more listening to him and our neighbour, Barney McGett-igan, as we passed the time on winter days in cold outhouses, plaiting straw ropes, sorting potatoes, riddling and bagging them.

They grumbled over the price of potash and talked about a war in some faraway place called Korea. They discussed everything from God to Gracie Fields or the possibilities of the Atomic Bomb. I remember my grandfather once saying, 'Sure wouldn't a man be better off in his grave with a bomb like that about.'

They weren't educated men who read newspapers and they lived in a time before mass media but they were able to look at the world around them in their own distinctive way and hold opinions informed by their own commonsense.

Vincent. J. Doherty lives at Palmer's Green, London. This is his third time to be published in the Ireland's Own Anthology of Winning Short Stories. *He was twice a previous prize-winner in the Memoirs category.*

Eaten Bread

By Alan O'Brien

Peggy had run the traditional corner shop for many years and it was an integral part of the local community. Now as Declan accompanies her on her final journey he reflects on the central role Peggy and the shop had also played in his life …

THE LONELY sound of the bell greeted the small funeral procession as it wound its way up the hill to the church. From the church you could see the harbour and the whole sweep of the bay. The church had been built on a hill, and it was said that it was built there as it would be the last thing the sailors and fishermen would see as they sailed out, and the first thing they would see as they returned.

Peggy was making her final journey to the church, a journey she had made every Sunday during her working life and then every day when she retired, until she went into the nursing home. Her death, when it came, was a happy release as her body had long since ceased to function on its own and even the most basic of tasks required the help of the nursing staff.

Her mind was still as sharp as ever and this only added to her torment as her dignity had been stripped from her. Despite the nursing staff being as professional and as caring as they were, life in the nursing home was a constant embarrassment to her. After a life of hard work and self reliance, the loss of her independence hurt her most of all. She had often said that it would have been much better if her mind had gone and her body had remained intact.

Declan used to visit her as often as he could and now as he walked behind the hearse he couldn't help but feel a pang of guilt as lately his visits had become more and more infrequent.

He had been busy with the renovations to Peggy's shop, his shop now. He was extending the little corner shop into a mini-market. The days of the little corner shop were gone and his only hope of survival was to increase the size of the shop so he could increase the range of products on offer. He had bought the house next door when it had come up for sale.

Declan smiled to himself as he remembered when he first went to work in the shop. It had been as a schoolboy, when, after school he would pack shelves and weigh potatoes into quarter-stone and half-stone bags. Little did he think then, as he worked to get the money for a new bicycle, he would end up owning the shop.

Nearly every boy and girl in the neighbourhood had, at some stage, worked in the shop, some for long periods of time but some for just a few weeks because, for some of the boys at least, the desire to play football after school was greater than the desire to earn money. Some were bringing much needed extra cash into houses that had large families.

The shop was at the end of a row of terraced houses and what had once been the front room and kitchen had been converted into a shop with the living quarters now upstairs. Over the years a concrete building had been erected in the back garden and this acted as the stores.

Declan remembered how he loved it when the Sweet Man used to come and he would be sent out to help him bring in the order. The Sweet Man would always give Declan some 'samples' as he called them, to try. These 'samples' were, in fact, usually the contents of a box that had burst open when it had fallen off one of the shelves in the van. Declan didn't care, they tasted just the same as the completely packaged ones.

When the minerals were being delivered Declan would have to open the back gate which led to the lane behind the shop. The Mineral Man would bring the crates of soft drinks on his hand truck down the lane, in through the gate and into the stores. When it was all brought in they would check through the delivery together and make sure the order was correct. Declan would then have to sign the delivery docket and this made him feel very important.

Gradually he was brought in to the shop to serve at the counter. After a while, when he had served his apprenticeship, he was at the counter almost all of the time. He enjoyed working at the counter as he relished the trust that Peggy placed in him.

Peggy knew all her customers and all their children by name. She had an incredible, almost photographic, memory and could recall events with such detail that she was often called upon to settle an argument (and sometimes a bet) or clarify an event that happened years ago. She loved to talk of times past and now, as Declan watched the coffin being taken out of the hearse, he realised how foolish he had been that he hadn't the sense to write down all the gems of historical information she had relayed to him.

As he stood there he could see two of Peggy's best friends, Mary Brown and Mary Clarke, known as Mary B and Mary C, crying as the new priest said prayers over the coffin before they went into the church.

Declan remembered how he used to enjoy when Mary B and Mary C came into the shop. They would both have shopping lists which Peggy would give to him while the three women were engaged in conversation. He would get two cardboard boxes and pack them with the orders. When he had the lists complete he would bring the boxes and sit them on the counter and write Mary B on one and Mary C on the other.

He would lift the hinged flap of the counter so he could put the boxes into Mary B's pram. Mary B's children were well past needing a pram and there would almost always be some remark or other, which at the time the young Declan didn't quite understand, regarding the contents of the pram being easier to come by and easier to manage than the original contents.

Declan would write the details of the shopping lists into 'The Book' and the groceries would be paid for at the end of the week. It was only when he had bought the shop and came across some of these

'Books' that he realised how much credit Peggy had extended to her customers. He also found out that a substantial amount had never and would never be paid.

He recognised some of the names and it galled him to see these same people walking around with their head in the air without a care in the world. He knew that Peggy must have seen them too but she never did anything to recover what was owed to her. He remembered and understood what his own mother had meant when she said that Peggy had kept the townsfolk going during the war years.

The undertakers brought the coffin to the foot of the altar and the priest said more prayers. He then went to the lectern to deliver a short homily before he started to say the mass. Declan noticed that the priest was at least clever enough to avoid the usual cliché sentence whereby the esteem in which the deceased was held was reflected by the large attendance in the church.

Instead he went on to say how bravely she bore her illness and now she would be joining her husband, Denis, who had tragically drowned at such a young age while fishing in the bay.

Declan could feel the irritation growing. The fact that the priest had used the name Denis showed how little he had known about Peggy. If he had spent any time at all with Peggy he would have used the name Dinny. Even Declan referred to him as Dinny although he had died long before Declan had started to work in the shop. When Peggy spoke of Dinny it was as if he had just stepped outside for a few minutes. He was always present in her life.

It irked Declan that the priest was talking about Peggy as if he had known her for years when it was plain to anyone who knew her that he didn't know her at all. It would have been better if he had come straight out and said that since he was new he didn't know Peggy himself but from what he had been told by those who did etc, etc.

While the mass was proceeding Declan was dealing with some mixed feelings. He was feeling a sense of relief that Peggy's suffering was at an end although he was sorry to see her go. He was feeling annoyed that after all she had done for so many of the townsfolk they hadn't even bothered to come to her funeral, and then this priest trying to make out he knew even the most obscure of his parishioners when he clearly hadn't a clue about her.

Then his mind drifted back to the time he had brought his brand new bike to show off to Peggy. She was so delighted that he hadn't squandered his earnings and instead had purchased such a beautiful bicycle. She had shown suitable amazement at all the gears and was very impressed as he explained that he could easily ride up even the steepest of hills without any trouble.

She started to laugh and began to tell him about the bicycle her husband had as a young lad. 'It was a big upstairs model,' she beamed. She went on to say that there was no such thing as gears on bicycles in those days and when you came to a hill you had to get off and push. 'And you know in this town you are either going up a hill or going down a hill, so poor Dinny spent as much time pushing it as he did pedalling it'.

He remembered her telling him that when Dinny was a young lad he used to cycle out to the country to collect milk from the farmer. The milk would be carried in cans on the handlebars of the bike that he would then deliver door-to-door. This had to be done twice a day, morning and evening, and sometimes in the evenings when he was dispensing the milk from the can into the customers jug, they would put their hands around the can to make sure it was still warm. That way they knew the milk was fresh and was not left over from the morning's milking. How times have changed, he thought, now milk is pasteurised, homogenised, semi-skimmed and some with vitamins added.

The mass ended and the coffin was to be taken the short distance to the grave within the church grounds. Declan stepped forward and volunteered to help carry the coffin to its final resting place. Suddenly he felt it was important that Peggy had someone she knew to walk the last few steps with her.

The final prayers were said and the few people who were there dispersed. On his way home the old saying 'eaten bread is soon forgotten' kept going over and over in his head. The saying was very apt in this case as when Peggy had the shop she was always one of the first people to arrive at the house when someone in the neighbourhood had died. She would bring a present of some bread and ham for sandwiches, and a bottle of whiskey.

Then a thought struck him. He knew a way that Peggy's name would be remembered. There had never been a name over the shop, just a sign advertising one of the daily newspapers. Now there would be a name over the newly renovated shop, it would be called Peggy's Mini-Market.

Alan O'Brien is from St. Manntan's Park, Wicklow. He is a regular contributor to the Ireland's Own *magazine. This is his first time to be published in the* Ireland's Own Anthology of Winning Short Stories and Memoirs.

Making Things Happen

By Margaret Cameron

She was surprised how relieved she felt to be alone at last … since Paul's illness, then his death followed by the wake and the funeral, there had been a constant traipsing of visitors coming and going …

'WILL YOU BE alright Mother?' 'Yes, yes, of course I will,' said Kathleen. 'You have your own life to get on with. You have been very good staying so long.' It had been five days since the funeral and Maureen was now thinking of her own home and family.

She lifted her case and coat. 'I'll put these in the car, be back in a moment.' Kathleen shivered as the rush of cool air came in through the open front door. She was a tall, lean woman who carried herself well even now in her seventies. 'I'm determined not to develop a hump,' she often said, much to the amusement of her cronies. Her dark hair streaked with grey was worn short and neat.

Maureen stepped back into the hall bringing the autumn air with her. It was a cool but pleasant September afternoon with a mellow sunshine struggling to bring a little warmth. 'I want to hit the road before the evening traffic.'

Maureen wrapped her arms around her mother and the tears dripped on the nape of Kathleen's neck. 'I miss Dad so much.' Maureen's voice was muffled and vexed.

'I know dear,' said Kathleen, 'but it had to be, we wouldn't have wanted Dad to suffer any longer.' They stood in an embrace then Kathleen said briskly, 'Now, off you go, I'll walk out to the car with you.'

Kathleen stood waving as her daughter drove out of the avenue and out of sight then she turned and went indoors.

She was surprised how relieved she felt to be alone at last. She closed her eyes and gave a deep sigh. Since Paul's illness, then his death followed by the wake and the funeral, there had been a constant traipsing of visitors coming and going. She had felt overwhelmed by the constant pressure of having to put on a good face every morning and to be the perfect hostess, the dignified widow.

Of course she never could have managed without the support of her daughter but she never did like that husband of hers and was glad when he returned home after the funeral.

Alone now, she wandered around the rooms fingering a photo here and an ornament there – reminders of her 37 years of marriage to Paul. They had built up a cosy home together. It was a bungalow with two reception rooms and three bedrooms. As the years went on and money became more plentiful they had added a paved patio area. She had liked this bungalow from her first sighting of it and was happy here.

It was she who had, in fact, travelled up to Belfast on the Enterprise and viewed a few properties and new developments and on seeing this bungalow knew it was the one and secured the deal.

She had been living in Dublin for a number of years at the time and sharing a flat with two other girls in a big, rambling house that was let out in a number of flats. Although brought up in Greystones, once her education was completed she was eager to cut the restrictions of home life and fend for herself. She had obtained a job as a secretary in a group surgery and had found a flat to share with other girl-friends.

The world was new and shiny then. They had been fun, care-free years. Time passed dancing and romancing and whilst she had her share of romances it was her flatmates whose love affairs had blossomed into marriages. Kathleen found that she was forever seeking new flatmates. Lately the flatmates had been others' friends and she didn't have the same relationship or a lot in common with them. They were much younger and they made her feel staid.

Of course the tenants of the other flats in the house came and went also. There had been several young men from the other flats with whom they had partied and fooled around with but nothing serious developed.

She knew that Liam and Michael in No. 3 had been on the hunt for a third person for some time. 'We've got a new bloke coming on Monday,' Liam said one evening as they sat around the kitchen table drinking coffee in the girls' flat.

'What's he like?' was the immediate chorus.

'Tall guy called Paul. He's from Limerick and works for a computer firm; doesn't say too much, a bit hesitant.'

'Oh we'll bring him out of himself,' laughed the girls.

'I like the tall silent type,' said Mary.

However the weeks passed and the new lodger declined the invitation of his pals to visit the girls although they had seen glimpses of him and had built up a word picture from Liam and Michael. He was 28 and was a good cook. No, he hadn't a girl-friend, in fact his fiancée was killed in an accident.

'Poor guy, maybe that's why he doesn't want company.'

It was Kathleen who finally got him to visit. She waylaid him on the stairs one evening. 'Hello Paul, I'm Kathleen from No. 6; why don't you come up tonight with Liam and Michael to our flat for a coffee?'

'I am going …' There was a hesitation, he blinked his eyes and his mouth formed a word but no sound came.

'… to come up … tonight,' Kathleen finished eagerly, more out of discomfort. 'Oh great, I'll tell the others,' she added.

He looked startled but then his face broke into a quirky smile and he quietly said, 'Okay.'

Oh, heavens that smile, thought Kathleen as she bounded up the stairs. It had been a pleasant evening but Paul was quiet and didn't really engage in the conversation, just smiled and nodded a lot.

'Well, what did you think of Paul?' asked Mary. 'He really is handsome.'

'Sure he said nothing for himself as Kathleen kept answering for him,' said Carla. She clinked the glasses together by the stems as she cleared the coffee table.

85

I did not,' Kathleen said sharply.

'You did, you kept prompting and finishing his sentences for him.'

'I think Kathleen fancies him,' said Mary as she flicked the tea towel at Kathleen.

'He's too young for her.' Carla glanced at Kathleen, 'You must be seven or eight years older than him.'

'Thanks very much Carla, I can always rely on you to spell it out.' Kathleen's face was flushed in anger.

The occasional visits continued and then one evening the girls received a written invitation to No. 3 for a fork supper. They were each excited.

Paul was a competent cook and had also transformed the untidy flat into a more habitable place. The sofa was now strewn with cushions instead of jackets, anoraks and sweaters.

'We are civilised now,' said Michael, 'and can invite guests in.'

It was an enjoyable evening and Paul appeared more at ease and in his comfort zone. 'Come on Paul, give us a song,' said Michael. 'Yes, he can sing, wait 'til you hear him.'

Paul wasn't hard to coax and astounded the girls by his singing of 'China Doll.'

'Goodness, you sound like Brian Coll of the Buckaroos,' said Carla.

His singing added to the tone of the evening and he and Kathleen seemed to gel while tidying up in the kitchen. Kathleen instinctively came to his aid by filling in the hesitant words. That was the start of their relationship and soon they became a couple.

However, as one relationship developed the relationship with her flatmates seemed to sour since Paul came on the scene.

'I don't understand why you are so nasty Carla. I could understand if he was 18 but he is 28. He is not my toy-boy.'

But Carla continued making snide remarks and Mary too had made the odd caustic remark about Kathleen monopolising Paul.

Kathleen felt peeved as it was she who had originally acquired the flat all those years back and now felt she was being ostracized and she couldn't think of a way of getting rid of them.

Her world further crashed when Paul announced that he was being transferred to the firm's Belfast branch in four months' time, allowing for his replacement to be appointed. She couldn't imagine life in the flat with those two once he had gone. She would have to move.

Her relationship with Paul was loving and affectionate. They held hands when they went walking in the park and he always sat with his arm around her shoulders when seated, especially in the cinema.

She knew how she felt about him - she loved him. But how did he feel about her? Did he only regard her as a soul mate? She needed to know now that he was leaving. They blended together so much so that she intuitively knew what he was thinking and going to say. On the odd occasion when she got it wrong, the mistake would be erased by laughter which brought them closer together. But he had never made his feelings known. Neither did he discuss his former fiancée.

Kathleen's days now were fraught with wondering what the future held for her. Some days she convinced herself that he really cared and wouldn't leave without her. She was now part of him and he relied on her.

It was a soft June evening when they returned home from an outing. They lingered and stood in an embrace by the chestnut tree where he parked his car. He had been talking about the transfer.

'Will you…' he stopped in mid-sentence and Kathleen heard her voice say, '…marry me?'

She froze, oh God, I've voiced my thoughts not his. She looked up into his eyes and saw the same startled expression she had seen a year earlier. She dropped her arms but he pulled her closer in embrace and asked, 'Will you?' He smiled down at her while he waited.

'Yes,' she whispered.

Things moved swiftly after that but she never dared to ask if she had read his hesitation correctly. She didn't want to know.

A date was set for the wedding and Paul was agreeable that she should go house hunting in Belfast so that they would have a home when she obtained employment there. Her flatmates were nonchalant about her news and quickly turned their attention to plans for a replacement.

Within the four months everything slotted into place and she and Paul settled into their new environment, new employment and married life.

The cool September evening gradually crept into dusk as Kathleen seated herself in the armchair by the window, glad to be alone with her thoughts. She gazed out the window at the distance but her mind's eye was pondering the 37 years with Paul.

When no baby arrived Paul was content to adopt and Maureen became the centre of their life. They had worked, saved and had an enjoyable social life. They made new friends and some of their original neighbours had passed on. They continued to speak as one and Paul became very popular at gatherings when he was called upon to sing 'China Doll' and other favourites. In later years he took to singing, 'I'll take you home again Kathleen' and she felt nostalgic for Dublin but she knew in her heart she wouldn't move back. Hadn't she steered matters to get away.

At times over the years she was tempted to ask Paul outright if he really had intended to ask her to marry him or had she prejudged the situation. She decided to lock this niggling question away every time it raised its head.

Now he was gone, she would never know.

It's time I locked the box for good and threw away the key, she thought. She closed her eyes and sat peacefully in the gathering dusk. Sometimes you have to make things happen, she thought ruefully.

Margaret Cameron is from Old Holywood Road, Belfast. Her work has appeared regularly in the Ireland's Own *magazine. This is her second time to be published in the* Ireland's Own Anthology of Winning Short Stories.

First Love

By Maura Connolly

Unknown to us she refused to put John's calls through and when I asked for his number she said 'no answer' and hung up. I was broken hearted and could not understand why John did not phone me or even accept my calls.

'WANT TO try, Gran?' asked my grandson, Tim.

'Ah, no thanks love' I replied as I watched him play a game on his dad's mobile phone. I could not even imagine my arthritic fingers fumbling with those little buttons.

'Tell me about the phone in the old days, please Gran.'

'Our phone was the only one in the village' I said and my mind went back to my young days and the old phone in our draughty hall and to my first love.

'Our phone sat on the hall table. It was a big black shiny hand piece. You put one end to your ear to listen and spoke into the other end. It was attached to a cradle and the cradle was wired to the wall.

'Phone calls were very expensive in those days, you had to pay for to install it along with the cost of the phone and you had to pay to rent the line. Ours was mostly used in times of emergencies to call the doctor or a vet for a neighbour or an occasional call to relatives who lived far away.

'Our Aunt Mary lived in London and when we were in bed at night we often heard our mother chatting on the phone. My father constantly reminded her of the cost of the calls. All the neighbours used our phone. That's the way it was in those days. Neighbours helped one another …'

My grandchildren listened attentively as I became lost in my memories.

The exchange was in the Post Office three miles down the road from our house. All calls that came to our phone went first to the exchange and Mrs Parker, the Post Mistress, put the call through. It was well known that she listened in to the conversations.

John came to stay with his Aunt Hilda for the summer holidays. It was 1960 and I had just turned 17. I fell head over heels in love. September came too soon and he returned to Dublin to work in his father's shop. I was waiting for confirmation of a place to commence my nursing career in London but in the meantime there was the phone. John phoned as often as he could.

My grandchildren got fidgety. They were too young to be bothered with romance but I continued with my story.

In the big cities they had phone boxes. The phone was like ours except there was a box with a slot where you put in the money. When your money was used up, the phone just went dead. John discovered that the phone in the phone box at the end of his street was broken and you could talk for ever for free. The phone became our best friend.

Mrs Parker was very annoyed. She was not used to her exchange being so busy and I expect to her, our chats were boring. When she met my mother at Mass she told her about the calls. Unknown to us she refused to put John's calls through and when I asked for his number she said 'no answer' and hung up. I was broken hearted and could not understand why John did not phone me or even accept my calls.

'She was a wicked lady' said Tim.

His younger sister piped up, 'He should not have phoned without putting money in the box.' She was preparing for her First Holy Communion and was very aware of what was right or wrong.

'Maybe you are right child' I replied.

The years passed. I went nursing to London and returned to Ireland to work in the local hospital. Then I met and married your granddad, Pat. I never met John again. His aunt sold the farm while I was in London and I lost all contact. It was years later I met Mrs

Parker when she was in the hospital on an 'Out Patient' visit. She asked me did I ever keep in touch with that 'young Smith fellow from Dublin?' It was a long time ago so I just said 'No' and wished her well with her doctor's appointment. My mind wandered back to bygone days and to John and the smile that made my heart sing.

'Gran, why do you look so sad?' asked young Tim. 'Do you not love granddad Pat?'

'Of course I do, Tim. Now off with you, I hear your dad calling.'

Tim and his dad are gone home and I am still thinking of that summer and what might have been. Pat and I have a good life and a happy marriage but there is always something special about first love.

*Maura Connolly is from Naas, Co. Kildare. This her second time to be published in the I*reland's Own Anthology of Winning Short Stories. *She was first published in the 2012 edition.*

Home is Where the Mind is

By Phil Chambers

Nora comes to the rescue of a confused old man in the park who doesn't remember where he lives; gradually she pieces his story together and it transpires his condition is the result of shock …

'ARE YOU alright mister?' said the young woman to the old man who was sitting on the park bench. Each morning, after walking her seven-year-old son Sean to school, she would then walk three times around the park as part of her keep fit routine. On her first lap she had noticed him standing by the pond. This time when she came around, he was sitting on the bench, with a vacant look on his face.

She wasn't sure what had drawn her attention to him; it was probably the clothes he wore – a lightweight suit, shirt and tie, clothes not suited for the cold spring wind that was whipping around the pond on that morning.

'I don't know … do I know you?' replied the old man.

Now that she was nearer to him she could see the confusion on his weather-beaten face, the remaining strands of white hair being blown across his eyes.

'No, you don't,' replied the young woman, 'I just noticed you sitting here in the cold and wondered if you were alright – my name is Nora.'

'I don't know,' replied the man, 'I don't seem to know anything anymore. I can't even remember where I live.'

'Oh dear, that's so sad, you poor man,' said Nora.

Realising how cold it was getting, her first thought was to get the man in out of the cold.

'I think, what you need now is a good hot cup of tea,' said Nora, 'There is a little coffee shop around the corner, would you like to come with me? At least it will be warm in there.'

'Thank you – yes – that would be lovely,' replied the man.

'This is a nice cosy table here in the window alcove – it even has a radiator. Now you just sit there and I will get the tea.' said Nora.

When she arrived back with a pot of tea and two scones he was still sitting there with a lost look on his face.

'There we are now,' said Nora, as she poured the tea, 'can you tell me your name?'

'Thank you Miss' said the man, 'I'm Gerry Sullivan.'

'So you don't know where you live Gerry,' began Nora, 'maybe you could describe it to me!'

'Oh it's a big house beside the river – the river where we used to paddle and sail our boats when we were young. In the deeper parts we would catch fish to eat. But sometimes the fish would be poisoned from up the river and we would have to stop fishing. I think the poison came from the tannery,' said Gerry.

'Did you live near the Botanic Gardens? ' asked Nora, remembering the recent fish kill in the river that ran through the Botanic Gardens and hoping for a connection for the man's memory.

'Botanic gardens? No, my father grew all the potatoes and vegetables needed for our family, remember there were eight children to be fed and food was rationed because of the war.' said Gerry.

'Life must have been very difficult during the war,' said Nora, trying to follow his thought process.

'Oh yes. Do you not remember the empty roads? Only the doctor, the policeman and the priest had cars due to the petrol rationing. The roads were our playgrounds –surely you remember that?'

'Why was the petrol rationed?' asked Nora, as she refilled his teacup.

'Sure all the petrol was being sent to England for the war effort. We had only enough here for the "Emergency", as it was called,' said Gerry.

'And what kinds of games did you play on the roads, Gerry?'

'Can you not remember? In the summer you girls played skipping

93

and hopscotch and we played soccer with an old tennis ball. Remember how annoyed we would get when a car would be seen coming down the road? In the winter, remember how we would pour buckets of water on the road and when it froze we had our very own skating rink. And of course we hated when the street lights went out at night,' said Gerry.

'Why was that Gerry?' asked Nora.

'Because of the Blackout that was in force - we didn't want the German bombers to be able to see the city and if they came down low we hoped the Barrage Balloons that hung over the harbour would catch them,' said Gerry.

'So you didn't always live here!' said Nora, trying to bring him back to the present.

'But I don't know where I live,' said Gerry.

'Can you remember how you got here?' said Nora.

'How I got here?' said Gerry. 'But I got here by train, of course, it was very exciting. All that steam coming from the chimney and sparks coming from the fire in the engine.'

'That must have been very exciting,' said Nora, 'did you come to Dublin to work?'

'Yes, there was very little work in Cork in those days. Lots of my friends had to leave Cork to get work,' replied Gerry.

'Have you been living in Dublin ever since?' asked Nora.

'Yes, I think so. Is this Dublin?' asked Gerry.

'Yes it is, Gerry. Tell me, did you marry a Dublin girl?' asked Nora.

'Marry a Dublin girl? – God no. Sure there were no Dublin girls in Cork in those days; Betty is from Cork. Her mother used to bake on the sawdust fire – no need for thermostats in those days,' replied Gerry.

'Tell me about the sawdust fires, Gerry', said Nora, – her curiosity getting the better of her.

'You don't remember them?' said Gerry. 'Well, with fuel shortages the main source of heat was either turf or timber – wasn't it? When the timber was cut the sawdust would be saved. My father would

94

then get an empty thirty-gallon oil drum, take the lid off and put holes in the bottom. He would then place a pole down the middle of the drum and then pack the sawdust all around it. He would then extract the pole and light the sawdust from the bottom.

'When the fire was burning – and it could burn all day – my mother would bake and cook on it all day long; brown bread, soda bread and "Spotted Dick" (soda bread with raisins).'

'And does your wife still bake, Gerry?'said Nora.

'Betty bake? How could she - isn't she in the hospital,' said Gerry.

'Oh I didn't realise that,' said Nora, 'can you remember the name of the hospital?'

'The doctor said it wasn't serious – that she would be fine. But he was wrong, wasn't he? Now who is going to look after me?' said Gerry.

'Were you with your wife this morning, Gerry?'

'That was when that other doctor told me that she wouldn't be coming home. Why did he say that to me? I got such a shock I don't seem to be able to cope with it all,' said Gerry.

Nora now knowing that his wife, Betty Sullivan, was in hospital, decided to slip outside and ring the Guards for help - they would be able to check with all the hospitals in the area. As soon as she returned, she ordered a fresh pot of tea.

'Would you like a sandwich Gerry?' she asked.

'That would be nice. Betty always made chicken and tomato sandwiches when we went to the seaside. She used to keep them fresh in a damp cloth,' said Gerry.

Ten minutes later her mobile rang. It was the local garda station to say that they had located the hospital where Betty was and that they were looking for Gerry. Apparently he had walked out of the hospital on hearing that his wife had died that morning and no one knew where he had gone to. Having advised her that the hospital was the local one, he told her that the couple lived on their own – their only son having died fifteen years previously. However, he understood that Gerry did have a brother still living in Cork and they were endeavouring to make contact with him.

The garda then said that they would arrange to have an unmarked car go and collect him from the café. However, when the garda came in to collect him, he was reluctant to leave and it was only when Nora promised that she would call to see him at the hospital, after collecting her son from school, that he agreed to go.

Nora then went to collect her son, Sean, and walked him home. Having given him his dinner she arranged with a neighbour to mind him for the afternoon. Next she rang her husband, Tom, to fill him in on the morning's excitement.

'Well, this must be a first – an eighty year old man! Normally you pick up stray cats and dogs!' was Tom's reply.

'Well Tom, you would be the first to admit that I just couldn't leave him sitting there – see you later,' replied Nora.

When she got to the hospital she discovered that Gerry had been admitted for observation. The doctor told her that Gerry had experienced some kind of catatonic shock on hearing that Betty had died and that it was some way of protecting himself from the loss of Betty. He told her not to be surprised if he could not remember anything about the morning. He also mentioned that they had given him a mild sedative.

On entering the room she could see Gerry tucked up in the bed – staring ahead. But as she approached the bed his eyes turned towards her and when he saw her he let out a cry. 'She's gone, Betty is gone. Oh my God what will I do?' With that he threw his arms around Nora and began to cry uncontrollably.

'That is exactly what he needed' exclaimed the doctor.

Eventually when Gerry regained his composure he said, 'Thank you for coming - Nora isn't it? - and sorry for messing up your blouse. Look at it – it's all wet and crumpled.'

'Now don't you be worrying about that. Sure it will dry out in no time,' said Nora.

As she sat there, holding his hands, Gerry told her how Betty and he had been married for over fifty years. They had met at a teachers dance in the National Ballroom. He had just qualified as a teacher and she worked in the Civil Service. It was love at first sight and they married a year later. They had just the one son who, unfortunately, had died fifteen years ago just as Gerry retired from teaching. Now she was gone – he was devastated.

Before leaving him she promised to call back later to see what the arrangements for Betty's funeral would be. The hospital social worker had been in contact with his G.P. and his neighbours. It appeared that his older brother in Cork was in a nursing home and couldn't travel.

'What are we going to do Tom? We can't just abandon the poor man,' said Nora, as they were having dinner that evening.

'Well Florence Nightingale, what do you think we should do?' replied Tom.

'We can't let him go back to his house after the funeral – that would be cruel. I think we should offer him the spare room on a day to day basis - until he adjusts to his new reality.'

The funeral was a very small affair. It appeared that Gerry and Betty kept very much to themselves and the neighbours all commented on their closeness – always walking hand in hand. Nora and Tom had arranged to bring Gerry to the local hotel for a meal after the burial.

'What am I going to do without Betty?' asked Gerry when they were seated in the restaurant, 'I don't know how to do anything.'

'Don't worry about that now Gerry; let's take one day at a time. How would you feel about staying with us for a while? We have a spare room and would love to have you with us,' said Nora.

'Oh I couldn't possibly do that – I couldn't impose on your generosity like that. I have my own home, but I suppose it will be very empty without Betty.' replied Gerry.

'Look Gerry' said Tom, 'this isn't charity - here is the deal. Our two kids are doing exams in a few months' time. Óisín is doing the Leaving Certificate and Grainne is doing the Group Certificate. Both are in trouble with their Irish subject. Now I understand from your neighbours that Irish was your speciality. So – you stay with us on a bed-and-breakfast arrangement and on a day-to-day basis and in return you coach both kids in the evening. How does that sound to you?'

'Well it doesn't seem to be a fair deal but thanks, I'm willing to try it for a day or two and see how it works.'

The days stretched into weeks and Gerry became 'granddad' to the family, especially to the three kids as he helped out, not only with the Irish, but by collecting Sean, the youngest, from school.

All too soon the exams started; however, it was two very confident students who faced the Irish exams and who came out from them smiling.

On the Saturday after the exams finished, Nora and Tom had a Bar-B-Q in the back garden to celebrate the end of the exams. It was a beautiful hot summer's day and the food was exceptional.

Later on in the evening, the kids having headed off to meet their friends, Tom and Nora and Gerry were sitting in the garden, enjoying the setting sun when Gerry, his work well done, slipped quietly away to join his beloved Betty.

Phil Chambers is from Stillorgan, Co. Dublin. This is her first time to be published in the Ireland's Own Anthology of Winning Short Stories.

Our Two Special Visitors

By Mary Weld

The pleasures of living were simple growing up on a quiet country road in the 1950s but some things leave a lasting impression …

I GREW UP in 'the country' in the fifties, which meant we lived about three miles from the nearest town. Our house was situated at the end of a straight road that stretched about half a mile before taking a turn. Traffic was scarce on it, with only the odd mechanically-propelled vehicle to be seen. The bicycle was the main mode of transport, and 'Shank's mare' was almost as popular as the bicycle for getting to the town.

One thing sure was that nobody passed by our house unnoticed, which always gave rise to discussion as we sat around the dinner table. 'Tommy Garvey must be collecting his pension today' or 'Ted Keogh was early for work this morning' or even 'did you see Jack Dunne driving a new car?' were all possible topics of the day.

Despite living on a quiet road in the country, we were guaranteed two special visitors every day. 'Old Mrs Higgins', a dear neighbour, came to fill two buckets of water from the well, which she would carry home on the handle bars of her bike.

When my eldest sibling was learning to talk she used to call Mrs Higgins "Ta-Ta", and of course we all followed suit. Ta-Ta was a small, slight woman, who always wore a navy-patterned cross-over apron. Her fine white hair was gathered into a bun and she wore small round glasses. She was a dab hand at making bread and taught Mammy to make the most beautiful brown bread you could imagine.

The other daily visitor was the postman, Neddy Farrelly, who cycled a full circle of about ten miles every day to deliver the post. Hail, rain or snow he arrived at our house around a quarter past eleven each morning. Mammy would have the table set and the kettle on the boil, while I watched for him to swing around the turn and come into sight. It was then time for Mammy to cut the freshly baked brown bread and make the tea.

The ritual of descent from his bicycle was the same every day. When he was passing the yard gate he would swing his leg high enough to clear the saddle, and when both feet were firmly on the ground the brakes were pulled and his bicycle would come to a sudden stop. He would prop it safely up against the wall, and as he made his way into the house the pebbles under his hard-wearing boots would crunch loudly.

Before taking the bag of post off his back he would check for our letters, leaving them on the oil cloth-clad kitchen table for Mammy to inspect. Putting his cap on the window beside him, he would stand the bag of post safely at his feet. By then the piping hot cup of tea was poured and he was ready to tuck in. He always added two spoons of sugar and milk fresh from the milking parlour, and stirred vigorously until it was ready for drinking.

I loved the clink of the spoon against the cup and the smell of sweetness coming from the hot tea. Mammy always said we did not need sugar in our tea, and we believed she knew best.

While Neddy buttered the brown bread the conversation would begin. I would watch him chew every bite, and how his ageing upper lip would furl around the brim of the cup as he sipped the sweet tea.

They talked about the news of the day, maybe about how his family were getting on, but the most popular discussion was always about the fortunes of the Kildare Gaelic football team. It was all about matches that were lost and matches that were won, and in particular what their chances would be for next Sunday.

Being children of the 1950s we knew that we were to be seen and not heard, so I would sit quietly, listen intently and watch every move the postman made.

But it wasn't all about bringing the post; occasionally Postman Neddy would bring my brother foreign coins and stamps to add to his collection. You see, his son was working at sea and would send home letters regularly from different countries. Mammy was always very interested in hearing where his son had been or where he was going to next. It was like a geography lesson.

Postman Neddy always kept one eye on the clock that ticked loudly on the wall, and once it struck half past eleven he would stand up, don his cap and reach down for his post bag. Lifting the strap over his head he would swing the bag around to his back, and at the same time thank Mammy, say goodbye and was gone.

All would be quiet once again. 'Clear the table', Mammy would say, and while I did I would already be looking forward to our two special visitors calling again tomorrow.

Mary Weld is from Clane, Co. Kildare. This is her first time to be published in the Ireland's Own Anthology of Winning Short Stories.

A Walk in the Park

By Linda Walsh

It was mother's 90th birthday party and everybody had enjoyed the occasion very much, especially mother. A chance meeting when leaving the hotel causes her to delve back into the past and, even at her age, she can come up with some surprises …

'DID YOU enjoy your party last night Mum?'

'I did, very much so, it was a lovely surprise.'

'I'm so glad; I was worried it would be too much for you, you are 90 after all.'

'There's no need to remind me, I am feeling every one of those years this morning, I might have overdone the dancing.'

'You certainly did, you were on fire. It was great to see so many friends and family, all together for a happy event instead of the usual sad gathering at funerals.'

We make our way slowly towards the reception desk in the Royal Marine Hotel in Dun Laoghaire to check out. There is a small queue so I seat my mother in the comfy sofa close by. I join some other members of my family and soon we are all laughing as we recall the happy events of the previous night.

It was a great success with lots of people from our childhood and long forgotten cousins showing up to celebrate this important birthday. It had been a late night in the resident's bar with a succession of merry trips down memory lane.

I glance across at my mother on the sofa and note that she has been joined by a woman I have never seen before. Their heads close together, the woman talking animatedly, my mother listening intently.

It's my turn at the head of the queue but before I turn away I see my mother patting the woman's hand gently. The woman's head is bowed and I sense that she is weeping.

I finish paying the bill and look back; the woman is gone.

'Who was that?' I ask some moments later as we make our way to the car.

Instead of answering my mother delves into her large black handbag. I think she is going to take out one of her linen handkerchiefs but instead she rummages in her purse and takes out a black and white picture and stares at it.

'Are you ok?' I am worried now; the earlier good humour seems to have disappeared. I hold open the passenger door and my mother eases her way onto the seat.

'I'm fine, but do you think we could visit the People's Park on the way home, just for few minutes?'

'Sure, no problem. The sea air will do us good, we certainly need it after last night.'

I pull out from the hotel car park and head towards the seafront. The fine weather has attracted lots of walkers this Sunday morning and I am lucky to find a parking space close to the park's entrance.

We link arms and cross the road at the pedestrian lights. My mother hasn't spoken since we left the hotel and I notice the photo is still clutched in her hand.

'Are you going to tell me what's going on? Who was that woman you were speaking to in the hotel?'

'Let's sit here near the fountain for a moment; I have a story to tell you.' My mother's voice is quiet but steady.

We sit companionably side by side for a while without speaking. People of all ages are walking around the park enjoying the unexpected October sunshine. The playground is filled with the laughter and cries of children as they kick their legs high on the swings or tumble down the slides.

In the seat opposite an elderly couple sit, the man reading a Sunday newspaper, the woman reading *'Ireland's Own'*.

My mother opens her hand and shows me the black and white photograph. It's a familiar face, my father as a young man, looking handsome in a tuxedo; he is facing slightly to his left, his hand extended. At the edge of the picture you can just see the swirl of a ball gown as his companion apparently flees the scene.

'Is this photo part of the story you said you wanted to tell me?' I am fretting a bit now, this mysterious silent woman beside me is not the mother I know.

'We used to come here all the time, you know.' My mother is smiling now, staring ahead, apparently oblivious to my question and the happy throng around her.

'Your Dad would get the No. 7 tram from Nelson's Pillar to the entrance over there. We would meet under the lamp post in the bandstand. Sometimes we would have a picnic in the park or just walk to the pier. It's such a lovely place, so full of happy memories for me.'

The sound of her voice and the unexpected autumnal sunshine causes me to close my eyes for a moment and I am immediately transported to another time. It's a fleeting moment but I can see my mother, dressed in a green cotton summer dress, a matching belt cinching her tiny waist, her brown curly hair brushed off her smiling expectant face. She waits for her man to appear through the blue wrought iron gates at the entrance to the park.

'You loved him very much, didn't you?'

'Yes, he was the love of my life, that's for sure.'

Silence again, but a contented one. I close my eyes and this time I see my father, bounding off the tram at the entrance to the park, spotting my mother and waving to her, rushing to her side. They kiss briefly, conscious of the people around, though in my mind's eye the park is filled with young lovers, making the most of the sunshine and their youth. I wonder why I never thought about my parents this way before, young, beautiful and in love. My father's sudden death some years before had left an empty space in our lives and I knew my mother missed him every day.

'Yes, I really loved him, but he was not my first love.'

My daydream ends and I am back in the here and now.

'It's silly really but I never thought of you having other boyfriends; I always assumed it was always just you and Dad, but of course you had other boyfriends, it's the normal way of things.'

'Oh yes, I had lots of beaus in my time I can tell you.' My mother has a mischievous smile on her face now and I start to laugh.

'That I can believe, I have seen the photos of you as a young woman, you were very pretty, always so smartly dressed and those ball gowns were amazing; there isn't the same glamour anymore.'

'I loved dressing up and going to dances in town on a Saturday night. There was the Crystal Ballroom and the Olympic Ballroom. My favourite nights were the dinner dances in the Gresham and the Shelbourne. We danced and we danced, it was magical.'

'Is that where you met your first love?'

Silence returns and I wait patiently for a reply. I can easily imagine the glamour of the nightlife in the 1950s, the photos of my mother and father on various nights out are carefully archived in a leather bound photo album and, though they are in black and white, the sense of fun and excitement shines through.

'His name was Peter O'Connor and I met him in Wexford on a visit home to see my sister. He was very good looking and very keen on me, we met every day and we were sad to leave each other at the end of my stay.'

'Did you meet up afterwards when you returned to Dublin?'

'We wrote to each other for months after and we met up as much as we could. Then one day he wrote to say that he was coming to Dublin and that he had something important to ask me. I knew then that he was going to ask me to marry him.'

'Would you have said yes to him?'

'I would have.'

I sit quietly for a moment taking this in, had my mother married this man I would not be sitting here listening to this story.

'What happened so?'

'I had just moved to another flat and I sent him the new address and I told him I would be waiting for him there. The day came and I dressed up in my finest dress and waited, but he never came, I never heard from him again. I assumed he had changed his mind and I was too proud to write to him to find out.'

'What on earth happened, did he have an accident?'

'Months later I met his sister by chance in Dun Laoghaire, she told me that he had left my letter behind on the train and had walked the streets trying to remember the name of the road, finally he gave up and went back to Wexford hoping I would write to him so he could explain. By the time he plucked up the courage to ask my sister for my address I had met your father and it was too late.'

'Goodness, how sad. Of course that would not happen anymore; mobile phones alone would have sorted that problem. It's amazing to think that your life could have been so different if he had not lost that letter. What happened to him, do you know?'

'He left for England and stayed there till he died. That was his niece I was talking to in the hotel, she told me he died last year in London. He never married and always talked about me, he called me his 'lost love'. He spoke about me right up to the end.'

'How on earth did she make the connection?'

'She works in the hotel, in the office, and noticed my name and age and just took a chance, she said Peter had a photo of me and had showed it to her often. She said she thought I should know that he had loved me for a very long time and that this was something she had to do for him too as she loved him very much.'

It's a sad story and I ponder the vagaries of life in which a small thing like losing a letter can change and shape future events in unexpected ways.

'Well, it's been a weekend of surprises that's for sure; do you want to head home now? I don't mind staying for a bit longer if you wish?'

'I am not finished my story, don't you want to know about this photo?'

'Good Lord, I had completely forgotten about that. Of course I would love to know about the photo.'

'That was the moment your Dad asked me to marry him, just as the photographer was taking the shot, I was so surprised that I ran off to tell my friends and messed up the photograph. The photographer printed the photo anyway, I love it, it's a special memory for me.'

We are laughing now as we make our way back to the car. It strikes me that despite having known my mother all my life she can still surprise me.

Linda Walsh is from Glencullen, Dublin. This is her first time to be published in the Ireland's Own Anthology of Winning Short Stories.

dangling from the nape of their necks. Many were wearing denim jackets and waistcoats but equally as many were sedately dressed in woollen jumpers and flannel trousers, and the ladies in staid dresses.

With the first chords of 'Caroline' the audience erupted and just like all those years ago. Heads started shaking to the music, soon arms were swaying in the air and everyone joined in as the band played all the old favourites. They played their heart out non-stop and by the time 'Down Down' and 'Rockin' All Over The World' were played, the floor was bouncing.

By the end of the night the denim clad and woolly-jumper-clad fans were head banging and arm swaying and dancing side by side. It was fantastic to see a band we had all grown up listening to actually perform in our local city. I guess at the end of the day, we're all old rockers at heart.

Fionnuala McNicholl is from Greysteel, Co. Derry. Her memoir is her first time to be published in the Ireland's Own Anthology of Winning Short Stories.

Two Ladies in Black

By Anne Anderson

A casual and rather ascerbic meeting to deliver a census form is the unpromising starting point from which an unlikely friendship develops between two women from very different backgrounds …

THEIR PATHS had never crossed before although Kathleen knew who Mrs Edwards was. Mrs Vance Edwards, Gertrude (Gertie to her very dear friends), was the lady who lived in Bloomfield Park, the widow of the late Captain Vance Edwards.

Kathleen tugged the frayed rope handle at the side of the door and after a momentary lapse could hear the faint sound of a bell ringing, far off in the bowels of the house. She knew that Mrs Edwards was at home because the ancient yellow Fiat that she drove, or rather raced around the village, was there, parked at a jaunty angle, as if she had abandoned it at speed.

She pulled the rope again and waited. Sure enough she could hear the excited yapping of a pair of Jack Russells and the indulgent endearments, 'There there, Buntlums, now now Oscar' as Mrs Edwards made her way to the front door.

'Good evening Mrs Edwards,' she said. 'I'm here to deliver your census form.'

'Humph,' said Mrs Edwards. 'I thought you were selling something. Down dears,' she said as the two Jack Russells ran and jumped at Kathleen. She might as well have said ATTACK! for all the notice they took of her command. Kathleen put her hand out to allow the dogs to get familiar and they settled.

'Census form? What am I supposed to do with that?' she asked.

'You must fill it in, and I will return to collect it, before the date there,' Kathleen said handing her the form.

'Humph, what a nonsense! What if I don't want to fill it in? It's of no use to me,' she said.

'I'm afraid you are legally obliged to fill it in, the information on the form ...'

Mrs Edwards interrupted Kathleen's well-rehearsed speech.

'Stop right there, I've heard the advertisement on the radio, no need to repeat it here. My husband has died since the last one.' Kathleen nodded sympathetically.

'I know,' she said. Then continuing in a manner most unlike her, she said, 'my husband has died since the last census too.' Mrs Edwards looked as if she hadn't heard her, but obviously must have as she continued, 'didn't know the fellow.'

'He was the postman, he delivered here, to Bloomfield Park' Kathleen said.

'Don't often see the chap who delivers the mail.'

With that she called the Jack Russells to heel and promptly closed the door. Kathleen turned and quickly sat into her car. She could feel her eyes welling up.

'How dare she dismiss you like that,' she said through clenched teeth to the myth of her husband who was always by her side, especially at times like this.

'Cruel old biddy! Stuff your census form,' and she drove off at speed, sending the gravel flying, just like Mrs Edwards herself might do.

Kathleen braced herself and made the return visit to Bloomfield Park to collect the census form on the due date. Once again she rang the bell and once again Mrs Edwards and the duo of exuberant Jack Russells greeted her. To her surprise the old harridan had the form filled in and ready for collection. She glanced over it as she was obliged to do.

'That's fine Mrs Edwards, thank you,' she said and turned to go.

'My hens are most prolific at the moment; may I offer you some eggs?' Mrs Edwards asked her. Kathleen was initially surprised and thought she couldn't have heard properly. She stood, inanimate for a moment, one foot on the step, the other suspended in the air.

'Eggs, I've loads of 'em. Would you like some?' She had heard correctly.

'That's kind of you, yes thanks, I'll take some eggs.'

'Wait there. Back in a jiffy.' Mrs Edwards closed over the door and disappeared. She reappeared quickly with a brown bag; there must have been a dozen plain and speckled eggs within, some with the merest trace of dirt still on.

'If you like them, come back next week. I've more than I could possibly use.'

Kathleen was as surprised as she had been maddened on the previous visit.

The eggs were delicious, as only eggs that come from happy hens can be. She hesitated but in the end decided that she would give Mrs Edwards a chance to be civil to her one more time.

The Jack Russells were getting used to her by now. They didn't make as much noise when Mrs Edwards opened the door.

'Ah back for more. Would you like some tea?' she asked.

Kathleen accepted the kind invitation and followed Mrs Edwards into the house. A faint musty air assailed her nostrils and three generations of Edwards with ruddy complexions and jutting jug ears scowled down at her from the walls. It could do with a good airing she thought as she followed Mrs Edwards down the tiled hall to the kitchen. It was a chintz palace, warm and free from stale air.

'Indian or China?' Mrs Edwards asked.

'Oh Lyons is fine, if you have it?' Kathleen said.

The weekly visits to Mrs Edwards began, ostensibly to collect eggs, which incidentally Mrs Edwards refused payment for.

'Are you lonely for your husband?' Kathleen asked Gertrude (they had reached that level of familiarity!) as they walked one day, along the path that meandered through her flower garden.

'I didn't like him very much, I liked his house, this house,' Gertrude replied. She gestured to the massive bulk of masonry behind them.

'You're shocked, are you?' she continued. Kathleen shook her head.

113

'No,' she said, 'nothing shocks me at this stage in my life.'

'Oh what virtue,' Gertrude said, 'judge me will you, make me feel better.'

'It's not my place to judge you,' Kathleen said, 'that's a job for the man above.'

'Oh no, not God!' Gertrude sighed. 'I'll tell you a secret. Poor Vance, I never loved him. And now I miss him dreadfully, the presence of him, his silly old habits, you know?' Kathleen didn't know, but she thought that there might be some sort of justice in it.

Kathleen told Gertrude about her grandsons, Jack and Ben. They were growing big and strong on the abundant supply of fresh free range eggs. The two ladies chuckled at the idea. They visited her regularly, showering her with little kindnesses, like carrying shopping for her, and mowing the small lawn at the front of her house.

'I've never seen my grandchild,' Gertrude declared.

'Oh no!' said Kathleen, thinking that to not see your grandchildren would be too awful to contemplate.

'My son has lived in Africa for many years, mining company, family business. The boy is five years old and I've never seen him.'

'Do you have a photo at least?' Kathleen asked.

Gertrude produced a photo from the overflowing dresser in the chintz palace. He was a tall (for his age) narrow, blond-haired boy, smiling from the dust of Africa. At least he didn't inherit the jug ears, Kathleen thought as Gertrude said, 'He looks like his mother, I believe.'

'Have you considered going out to visit your son?' Kathleen asked.

'My passport is out of date, I keep forgetting to renew. At any rate I don't much relish the thought of travelling to the Congo now. Been there, done all that.'

'You never said you'd been to Africa,' Kathleen said. She was in awe of the light hearted casual way that Gertrude drip fed her the details of her interesting, well travelled life.

'I was much younger when I was there last.' She looked far into the distance as if she was recollecting her time in Africa. 'They can come to me,' she said emphatically. 'They know where I am.'

Later that evening at Kathleen's home, her grandchildren called to her.

'What can we do for you this evening?' Jack asked her, meaning what chores could they do for her.

'Come here and give your granny a hug!' she said. They both hugged her and she held them tight and was slightly overwhelmed by the feeling of love she felt for them.

'No jobs this evening,' she said, 'I want you to tell me about your day, tell me every little thing that happened in it.' The two boys obliged, at times taking turns, other times both speaking at once, to tell her a more amusing version of what their day had actually been. Kathleen couldn't help but think of the little blond haired boy in the photo on Gertrude's dresser and she said a silent prayer of thanks for her own blessings.

She wanted to give Gertrude a gift, something to say thank you for the eggs and ... well, just thank you and I'm here if you need me. She decided on, without any fuss, the ideal gift, a cutting of an Old Rose that grew, no, held court, on her back wall. Her husband had planted it there when they were first married. It had grown from a cutting, she remembered that much, but where it came from exactly she didn't know.

In the early evening of a hot day, or an early morning for that matter, it filled the garden with the most heavenly scent and was capable of rendering the sniffer quite ecstatic. Kathleen carefully took cuttings and put them in a ziplock bag. Then she put together a generous bouquet of the sweet smelling bloomers and put them in water to keep them fresh until the next day.

Gertrude was positively cheered when Kathleen presented her gift.

'Bliss,' she cried. 'Hello Madame Alfred Carriere! Do you know, I had this rose in my garden at home, when I was a girl. Oh how it does remind me of ...' She paused to breathe in the scent from the bouquet. 'It reminds me of happiness!' she declared.

'We only ever called it the Old Rose, didn't realise it had a fancy name,' Kathleen said. She had never seen Gertrude Edwards so animated. She was pleased and slightly embarrassed that her gift had induced such a reaction in the normally staid Gertrude.

'I must plant the slips straight away,' she said. 'Make tea for us, will you, there's a dear,' and she went off to the garden and left Kathleen to make the tea. Friendship indeed!

The two ladies nurtured Madame Alfred Carriere with potash and manure and took great pride in monitoring her progress. There was so much work to be done in a garden as big as Gertrude's but Kathleen didn't mind one little bit. She quite forgot herself as she carried out the jobs that Gertrude assigned to her. And after all, she had her two boys, Jack and Ben, to help look after her own little plot.

The day that the Good News arrived, Kathleen was later than usual arriving to Bloomfield Park. Gertrude was waiting impatiently for her at the front door with Buntlums and Oscar.

'What is it, what's wrong?' Kathleen asked. Gertrude thrust a letter at her.

'Look what the postman brought, read it.'

'The postman ... oh you mean Jimmy ...'

'Yes, yes, Jimmy, the postman. Never mind that, please, read what he brought,' Gertrude repeated. Kathleen's eyes quickly darted over the sheet of blue notepaper. She looked at Gertrude; the two of them were strangely moved by the message in the letter. Gertrude's son was coming to visit and he was bringing his wife and her grandson with him.

'I am so pleased, that is good news,' Kathleen said.

'Will you bring Jack and Ben over when they come, they would be company for him?' Gertrude asked.

'That's a very nice idea,' Kathleen replied.

'Thank you,' Gertrude said. 'You will help, to prepare for their visit, I mean?'

'You know I will,' Kathleen said, and the two ladies went to water the roses.

Anne Anderson comes from Louth Village, Co. Louth. This is her first time to be published in the Ireland's Own Anthology of Winning Short Stories.

Harvested

BY SEAN O'DOHERTY

A national emergency has been declared on neutral Ireland during World War II and every able-bodied person is expected to help in harvesting the crops and the turf, and Paddy feels compelled to do his duty …

'WHERE DO YOU think you're going Paddy Downes?' asked Jane of her husband as he struggled into a pair of unfamiliar and undersized wellingtons. Paddy grunted as he finally forced his feet into the rubber boots. 'A bit on the small size but they'll have to do' he remarked. He fell back into the chair completely out of breath.

'Well?' his wife prodded.

'I'm off to help with the harvest,' was his proud remark.

'Help with the what?'

'The harvest, woman, the harvest! Haven't you been listening to the radio? It's a National Emergency! The call has gone out to every man in the country. It's my duty, my duty to my country!'

'Your duty is here Mr Downes! What about the toilet door that you've been promising to fix…not to mention the wallpaper in the bathroom that's been peeling off like an onion for the past five years. And don't forget your own harvest out back.' Jane placed heavy emphasis on the word 'harvest' and indicated a few sad rows of bruised cabbage and burnished potato stalks barely above ground.

Paddy's response was to straighten himself up rather grandly and announce 'Dear wife, national duty before domestic always, country comes first. Just as we came out in 1920 when we got the call, so too will we come out today!'

'Well, your very high falutin' all of a sudden…' but she was interrupted by the 'honk, honk' of a lorry outside.

'The lads are here, have to go!' and pushing past his wife, Paddy grabbed a fork outside the back kitchen and ran to the waiting truck.

'Here's Downser' called the motley crew of volunteers crammed onto the back of the truck. Paddy stretched his braces and threw the fork to an outstretched hand. He was then quickly hoisted aboard by many willing hands.

About twenty men stood on either side of the vehicle, hanging onto the railings. These were his workmates, his drinking mates and a few other acquaintances from the local 'Ranks Flour Mills'. Colloquially the firm was known as 'J. Arthurs' from the owners' name.

'Another Arthurs man,' shouted one of the boys.

Bob Hannigan, who had served in the Local Defense Force (the LDF) quickly assumed command. He was a small, wiry man with close cropped hair and a neat moustache.

'Good man Downes and welcome aboard. Got your lunch I hope.' He rapped a knuckle on the cab roof. 'Ar aghaid leat (on you go)', he ordered. There was a cloud of acrid smoke as the old Bedford coughed into life and a roar of approval came from the back of the lorry.

They soon left the environs of Limerick city and were into open country on the way to North Clare. Meadows of new mown hay and small plots of golden corn stretched on either side of the road. They passed neat white-washed cottages and could smell the turf smoke rising from every house on the early morning air. The Bedford struggled up Kilshanny hill. The landscape changed colour here. Ahead was a vista of brown bog with yellow furze, purple heathers and black ricks of turf, all interspersed with the white cannavaun, or bog cotton, bobbing in the breeze. This place had its own unique aroma. Salty breezes from the Atlantic shore mixed with the tangy damp air from bog hole and turf bank.

'Not a pub in sight' remarked Downes to his companion, Flynn. 'Thirsty miles to the nearest watering hole.' he joked. 'A man could die of thirst here.'

The lorry screeched to a halt at the bottom of the hill. 'All out,' shouted Hannigan as he drew a tattered map from his back pocket and spread it across the bonnet of the Bedford.

'This is Mick Frawley's bog. That's himself over there with the donkey.' An old man by a jaded beast slowly tipped his cap at the crew. 'Anyway, the area is divided into two sections. On the right is the Boston bog – don't ask me why it's called the Boston bog. On the left is Tulackeven up there just past the stream where the snipe is sitting. I'll take the Boston, anyhow.'

Hannigan looked over at Downes. 'Paddy, you're foreman in Ranks so you'll be well able to handle this lot here. It's two men to every barrow. We have to move all those stacks of turf up onto the main road. Ye'll all know that the bog is soft after the nights rain so be sure to keep to the paths. Beyond the main gate is fairly swampy. It's like a sponge and Frawley lost a calf there recently.' As if on cue Mick Frawley tipped his hat to the men once again.

The men set to work ferrying the black crop from the many banks across the 'Fionnach' (coarse grass), whilst avoiding the 'fuighre' (pool water). It was half way through the morning and Paddy's team had completed a good section of his allocated zone. 'Right lads, let's finish off that lot up there near the gate.'

The crew headed off as directed and worked with great gusto until Hannigan called a break with a sharp blast from his whistle about noon.

'Mrs Frawley,' he announced, 'in her generosity, has cups of tea and the like ready for us. I don't know how she manages with all that rationing and scarcity so be sure to show your thanks.'

The group nodded in agreement and wended their way up to the cottage.

'I see you're doing a bit of thatching there Mick.' Hannigan indicated the ladder against the gable wall but the conversation was cut short as the sweet aroma of freshly-baked apple tart and griddle cake assailed his senses.

A red and white checkered oilcloth adorned Mrs Frawley's carefully tended table. 'Come and get it lads,' she laughed.

Hannigan sat down and was just about to sink his teeth into a large helping of the steaming apple tart topped with a generous dollop of cream, when a loud roar rent the air. He dropped the fork back onto the plate and jumped up, spilling his precious tea on the tablecloth.

'That's someone in trouble yonder. Come on men, hurry!'

Mick Frawley suddenly became animated. 'Grab the ladder,' he ordered. 'Now get a few planks from the haggard and the rope by the door.' The men reacted quickly and followed his directions. They all ran together to the edge of Tulackeven and to their horror saw Paddy Downes up to his chest in the black mud and grappling for his life.

'Get the ladder across the bank! Pat, take a couple of men with those planks on either side. Hurry now, we don't have much time. Throw me the rope!' Mick Frawley made a quick lasso with the rope and flung it in the direction of the hapless man. Twice it missed its' target but on the third attempt Paddy managed to catch it and awkwardly pulled it down around his shoulders.

As they slowly hauled him out he fell across the outstretched ladder and many hands manoeuvered him into position. The sodden man was dragged from the black morass to safety, the bog hole reluctantly releasing its victim with a slurping, slobbering sound.

Paddy was covered in the dark, slimy, foul-smelling liquid. He looked weak and exhausted. 'Here, take a sup of this.' Mick had produced a small bottle from his pocket. 'It will help.' He raised Paddy's' head and forced some of the contents of the bottle into the wretched man's mouth. The effect was instant as Paddy coughed and spluttered and rose with a jerk to a sitting position.

'Take me home, take me home,' he whined as he collapsed back onto the ground.

Jane's' neighbour, Maggie, was enjoying a cup of tea and a chat with her dear friend when she noticed the men coming through the gate.

'Oh for the love of God Jane, you'd better take a look!'

'What is it?' Jane ran to the window. Her hands flew to her face and she raced to open the door. Paddy was carried in dripping black bog water across the hallway.

'Oh a stór, a stór, did you fall in?'

'Did I fall in? Well what do you think,' he said gruffly. 'Do you think the ground came up to meet me? What in God's name were you thinking sending me off to the bog? Have you no sense at all woman? Me harvesting days are over, I tell you! Me harvesting days are over!'

Sean O'Doherty is from Raheny, Dublin. This is his second time to be published in the Ireland's Own Anthology of Winning Short Stories. *He was a prize-winner in the Memoirs category in 2012.*

Wandering Star

By Margaret Clarke

Recalling the joys of youth hostelling and An Óige, the organisation that facilitated shoe-string travel around Ireland and Europe by young people.

M Y FADED blue-framed canvas rucksack is lovingly decor-
ated with familiar emblems from my backpacking days in
the sixties: a Welsh dragon, the little mermaid of Copen-
hagen, Iceland's blue lagoon, a Maltese cross, the Acropolis of
Athens, the red and white Monegasque flag and, less predictably, the
Red Hand of Ulster reminding me that although "The Troubles"
were in progress at the time, my friend and I were welcomed to
Ireland's northernmost province by everyone we met.

I had always wanted to travel but at 18 my income from my junior
secretarial post in the city left me with little after I had paid the bills
on my shabby rented bedsit. Then a friend told me about AN ÓIGE,
the Irish Youth Hostelling Association (IYHA), which was based at
Mountjoy Square in Dublin.

AN ÓIGE was founded on May 7, 1931, to encourage young
people to love and appreciate the Irish countryside through hostelling. Run by resident wardens, hostels provided basic overnight
accommodation in dormitories together and rudimentary cooking
facilities at an affordable price. In return, each hosteller was required
to do a simple chore such as sweeping a floor.

With our new rucksacks, a battered aluminium teapot, a fold-up
frying pan and a small camping-gas stove, my friend Eithne and I set
out on our first adventure. We took the bus to Glendalough where
we stayed in the hostel for one night, walking over the mountain

road to Aughavannagh the following day. We discovered that the food we cooked along the way was now called a "drum-up". We met hostellers of all ages and soon learned the ropes.

From then on, we hostelled every weekend all year round regardless of the weather and when we had seen most of Southern Ireland, we moved on to the North. The committee members from the Youth Hostel Association of Northern Ireland (YHANI) befriended us, regularly inviting us to their get-togethers both north and south of the border.

Our first trip outside of Ireland was to Scotland. We travelled by ferry from Larne to Stranraer and hitch-hiked up the coast to Ayr where we visited the Robert Burns Centre to learn about Scotland's national poet. Journeying up the West coast and down the East, we admired Glasgow's shabby Victorian architecture, paid homage to St. Columba on the windswept island of Iona, marvelled at beautiful Glencoe with its abundance of purple heather, took the ferry to the Isle of Skye and delighted in the elegant city of Edinburgh.

In January we attended the famous Viking Festival "Up Helly Aa" on the Shetland Islands, where we danced around a Viking ship which was set on fire.

Soon we were "old hands" at hostelling and with our confidence growing daily, we embarked on a month's trip around Europe. Sailing from Rosslare to Le Havre we set out on our proposed route, buying cheap bus and train tickets to get us around. Beginning with the elegant city of Paris, we headed northwards into Belgium with its old medieval towns.

We visited a cheese farm in the Netherlands, backpacked through Germany's Black Forest region, fell in love with Austria's chocolate-box scenery, ate Raclette in a restaurant in the Swiss Alps and travelled by water-taxi in Venice. We spent an exhausting and exhilarating four weeks taking in the principal sites and eating the local food.

The following year our travels took us to Scandinavia where we sailed through the majestic fjords of Norway. The endless fir forests, the mountains, glaciers and the stunningly beautiful villages were breath-taking. Near the Arctic Circle we stood in awe at the spectacle of the Aurora Borealis. We were impressed by Sweden's capital, Stockholm, with its royal palaces and gardens while Denmark's pastoral beauty was in complete contrast to its neighbours.

The high point of our trip was a visit to the remote Faroe Islands, which were a hiking paradise with their magnificent rocky coastline and thousands of seabirds. Near Torshavn, we watched as the crew of a whale boat captured and killed a large pilot whale before dividing it up among the islanders who used it for food.

For the next few years we hostelled throughout Europe for our annual holidays, visiting as many countries as our time allowed. After five summers of adventures, we felt it was time to hang up our rucksacks and try something else. A few months later, Eithne left for Australia and I moved to London where a new chapter in my life began. More than 40 years later, the memories of my hostelling days still remain with me.

I will always be grateful to the late Thekla Beere and the organizing Committee of AN ÓIGE, who 84 years ago set up the Irish hostelling movement, making it possible for young people like me to travel on a shoestring.

Margaret Clarke is from Wicklow Town. This is her first time to be published in the Ireland's Own Anthology of Winning Short Stories.

Ellen

By Cathleen Greaney

John Joe idolises his older sister, Ellen, who helps to rear him when mother has to go out to work. She goes away to boarding school and a local boy starts asking for her during the holidays. Quite suddenly Ellen is the subject of whispered conversations between her parents and then she disappears …

I WALKED DOWN the road of memories again and thought of Ellen. I was the youngest of five children who grew up on a small farm in the West of Ireland. I was born on the first of May, 1949, and christened John Joseph. Liam and Tom were packed off to Uncle Steve in Boston when they were in their late teens. My sister Mary married a local farmer when she turned eighteen. The only members of the family left at home were me and Ellen, apart from Mam and Dad.

I was four years old when Mam got a job as a housekeeper for Ms Cassidy who was the Principal teacher of the local primary school. I cried bitterly that first morning when Mam started her new job.

'Don't cry John Joe, we'll go up to see the new calf'. I followed Ellen up the boreen. Dad was up in the cowshed checking on the new black calf.

'Are you not in school today Ellen?' he asked gruffly.

'No, I'm minding John Joe for a few days. Mam knew you'd be busy with the farm'.

'Alright, off with the two of you then!'

We ran back to the house and Ellen made me a boiled egg and some toast.

Mam came home late that evening. She looked tired but she still made us a dinner of bacon and cabbage. Dad sat at the table in silence.

'I've something to say Pat' she ventured. 'Mrs Cassidy said that John Joe can start school. We need the money but we can't keep Ellen home. It's not fair on her'. He shook his head.

'Alright then, he's a bright little lad.'

The following morning Mam went to work and Ellen got me ready for school. We walked hand in hand to the grey one-storey building. It was about two miles down the road from our house. Ellen was in second class but Mrs Cassidy allowed her to sit beside me in Infants for the first day. We went to town that week and Mam bought me a pair of strong brown shoes and a red satchel and Ellen got some pink ribbon and a new plaid skirt.

Ellen always kept an eye out for me in school. I was small for my age. I remember one incident when Michael Joyce, a stocky built lad who was in third class, pushed me to the ground in the school yard. My knees were badly grazed; I fought back the tears. Our teacher Miss Clancy asked me what had happened.

'I fell Miss,' I lied.

After school that day Ellen got Mam's first aid box and cleaned the wounds. The following morning she had a word with Michael.

'He won't bully you again John Joe' she squeezed my hand. Whatever she said to him worked as he left me alone after that.

The seasons came and went. Summer was my favourite time, long balmy days, and no school. Ellen and I would walk up the old bog road carrying a brown canvas bag containing tea and crusts of brown bread and butter for Dad. Sometimes there would be some currant loaf that Mam had baked the night before if she was not too tired. She was still housekeeping for Mrs Cassidy.

Ellen and I would help foot the turf and she would push me around in the old wheelbarrow. We would gather bunches of wild flowers and purple heather and put them in jam jars which were placed on the window sills.

When I was eight years old Dad bought me a bicycle for my birthday. Ellen was going to the Convent School in the town that September.

That Summer I practised cycling up and down the boreen. One evening, I met Tommy Flaherty at the crossroads. Ellen and Mam had gone to town that day to buy her new school uniform.

'Where's your sister John Joe?' he asked.

'Gone to town' I shouted as I sped past on my bicycle

'Tell her I was asking for her' he called.

That evening Ellen tried on her new uniform – a wine jumper with a grey skirt and blouse to match. Mam tied back her black curly hair with a wine ribbon. Later we looked through some new comics.

'Tommy Flaherty was asking about you,' I whispered. Dad was sitting near the hearth smoking his pipe.

'Keep away from that fellow, he's too advanced for you.' He banged his fist on the table. Ellen turned bright scarlet and hurried out of the kitchen.

September came. It was decided that Ellen would stay in town with Dad's sister Aunt Molly, during school term. My heart sank.

'I'll write to you John Joe', Ellen promised. I crossed off the days on the calendar as she was not coming home until Christmas. I cycled to school every day and when the weather was bad Dad gave me a lift in his new van. I missed my sister. The house seemed so empty without her. She was gone about a month before I heard from her and then the letter came, a bright pink envelope.

'Dear John Joe, I miss you. I have made some friends at my new school. The nuns are very strict. Aunt Molly takes me to the pictures on Saturdays. Your loving sister, Ellen.'

One evening when I came home from school there was a large box on the kitchen floor. Inside was a tiny black and white puppy.

'He's yours son' Dad smiled. That night Spot slept at the foot of my bed. He could not replace Ellen but I felt I had a new friend.

Christmas finally arrived and Ellen came home for the holidays. On Christmas Eve, we went to midnight mass. It was a cold, frosty night and the sky was studded with millions of stars. Dad was called away to help a neighbour whose cow was calving but Mam came with us. Ellen had grown taller. She looked like a princess in a red coat with a fur collar that Aunt Molly had given her for Christmas.

The small church was packed. When Father Dooley was giving his usual long sermon, I noticed Tommy Flaherty sitting in the pew opposite us. He was staring at Ellen.

On Christmas Day we took a walk up the village while Mam was preparing the dinner. Spot ran ahead of us, it was like old times again. I was showing Ellen the new bullocks Dad had bought at the fair when a car pulled up beside us. It was Tommy Flaherty driving an old Morris Minor. His hair was sleeked back with Brylcream and he was wearing a leather jacket

'Would you like to go for a spin Ellen?' he grinned. She shook her head.

'Mam is expecting us home for dinner'

'Well then, hop in, I'll run you home'. Spot started to bark.

'Do you mind John Joe?' Before I had a chance to answer she popped into the car and I walked back to the house. I felt betrayed. Ellen was my sister and he had no right to drag her off like that.

Back home, Ellen was there before me, helping Mam to set the table in the front room. The best Willow Pattern china was set out. My sister Mary called with her husband John and the new baby boy in the afternoon. Dad helped me to assemble my new train set. Mary gave Ellen a hat and scarf set and a Roy of the Rovers Annual to me. Later we sat around playing cards. Mam and Dad reminisced about old times.

'Look at the lovely Christmas card Tom sent from Boston.' Mam showed the card to Mary. I knew that the card had contained 200 dollars as I had opened it.

On St Stephen's Day I went around the village with the wren. We got a few shillings and lemonade and Christmas cake at each house. Ellen stayed home that day. That evening she announced that she was calling up to Clancy's. Lily was in her class at the convent.

'Be home by eleven,' Dad ordered. He was in good form as he was going down to the local to have a few pints to celebrate the season. Mam and I sat by the fire and listened to the radio. At nine o'clock Mam stood up.

'I can't keep my eyes open any longer John Joe, I'm off to bed. Ellen should be home soon.' I dozed off on the fireside chair. When the clock struck ten, I went to bed hoping that Ellen would be home before Dad. I shut my eyes and fell into a restless sleep.

Ellen was running up the boreen in a long white dress. I ran after her but could not reach her. I awoke with a start. Something hit my bedroom window. I pulled back the curtain. Ellen was waving frantically below in the yard. I crept downstairs and undid the bolt.

'Sssh John Joe,' she whispered, her thin frame was shivering.

'How long have you been there' I queried

'Don't tell Mam and Dad or they will kill me.' We crept upstairs. I could hear Dad's snores on the landing.

I got up early and took Spot for a walk. Dad was sitting at the kitchen table when I returned. 'Pour me a cup of tea Ellen. What time did you come home, girl?'

'About 9.30' she lied. 'Lily and her sister walked me down the road.' I bit my tongue.

It was soon time for Ellen to return to Aunt Molly's. She promised to take me to the pictures some Saturday. 'You could come on the bus John Joe.'

Mam and I waved as Dad's van sped out of sight. January was a long gloomy month. February came. The birds started to sing again and the first spring lambs were born.

'Keep your eye on that dog,' Dad grunted. 'We don't want to be charged with sheep worrying'. Lately he was always complaining about something.

One day in late March I came home from school. Mam was sitting at the kitchen table with her face in her hands.

'What is it Mam?' I put my arm around her.

'Nothing child, I have a headache.' That evening Dad came home late. He had been drinking.

I went upstairs and lay on my bed. I could hear my parents arguing.

'What are we going to do, Pat?'

'She can't come back here' was Dad's gruff reply. There was something very wrong and I had no idea what it was.

129

The following Saturday Mam announced that she was going to town.

'Can I come too?' I begged.

'Another time John Joe, I have some business to attend to.'

'Will you be meeting Ellen, Mam? Remember we were to go to the pictures'.

'Stop pestering your mother,' Dad interrupted. 'Come up the village with me and we will clear out the cowshed.' We threw all the dirt onto a manure heap and put down fresh hay. Mrs Curran from the cottage nearby made us a flask of tea. I ran back to the van to fetch the sandwiches. A familiar figure stood in front of me blocking my path.

'How's Ellen, will she be home at Easter?' Something about Tommy Flaherty's expression made me uneasy.

'I don't know,' I muttered. 'I have to go'. He grabbed my arm. Just then Dad appeared and caught Tommy Flaherty by the collar.

'Keep away from my family or I'll kill you with my bare hands, you blackguard.' I had never seen him so angry.

It was dark when Mam came home.

'Did you see Ellen, did you buy me a surprise?' I asked.

'Yes, she's fine. She sent you some comics.' There was one question that had been bothering me for some time.

'Is she coming home for Easter?'

'No, she is going to stay at a friend's house in Galway.' Later that night I counted the money in my piggy bank. I had ten shillings saved. I resolved to go to town the following Saturday to visit Ellen.

I crept downstairs and sneaked out the front door. There was a thick fog covering the fields. It was about a mile to where the bus stopped at Poll a Síoga. Mags Curran and her daughter were waiting at the side of the road when I got there.

'Where's your mother,' Mags asked; 'Is she not with you?'

'I'm going to visit my sister, Ellen' I answered. Before she could interrogate me further the bus came. I made sure to sit at the back, well away from them.

I knew Aunt Molly lived off the town square. I had a vague memory of a white house with a green door as I had only been there once or twice with Dad.

'Is that Murphy's house' I enquired from a tall red haired youth who was pumping up a bicycle.

'Yes,' he nodded. I lifted the heavy brass knocker. The door opened slowly.

'John Joe, what on earth!' Aunt Molly stood staring at me.

'I've come to see Ellen,' I ventured.

'Come in child.' She glanced around before she closed the door. 'Did anyone see you?'

'I don't think so, why?' She gave me a glass of milk and a biscuit.

'Is Ellen up yet? Tell her I'm here.'

'Didn't your parents tell you? Ellen isn't here anymore.'

'Where is she?'

'She's gone to a boarding school in Galway.'

Aunt Molly brought me to the afternoon bus. Mam was white in the face when I got back home. Dad sat staring into the fire. Finally Mam broke the awful silence.

'Ellen has gone to a special place, John Joe. We don't know when she will be home.' I knew there no point in pursuing the matter any further.

'But she will be back won't she?' I tried to hold back the tears. She never did come back. I was told that my eldest brother, Tom and his wife, needed her to help with the children in Boston as they both worked. She was never mentioned after that. It was as if she was dead to them and she had to be dead to me too.

Cathleen Greaney is from Bray Co. Wicklow. This is her first time to be published in the Ireland's Own Anthology of Winning Short Stories.

My Troubled Heart

By Tony Lafferty

*John had always wondered why Mary had suddenly broken off
with him all those years ago, what had he done so wrong that
she had decided to cut all contact with him?
Now at last, accidentally, he was to get some answers …*

JOHN DELANEY was a thirty-six-year-old, wealthy bachelor, whose life had suddenly become filled with calamities that were upsetting his usually very ordered life. Almost everything in his life appeared to be either going wrong – or like his car this morning – breaking down, causing him no end of problems.

John could have called a taxi but chose instead to use the bus, which he was well aware could leave him late arriving at his work. But the devil was in him this morning, and as he was the manager, coming in late wasn't a problem. Anyway, he thought, it has been years since he last used public transport.

It started to rain as he began the short walk to the bus stop; he rang his personal secretary Helen, using his mobile phone. 'Helen,' he began, when she answered, 'My car won't start, so will you ring the garage for me, and tell them to come and collect it.'

'Okay John' said Helen, 'I will do that. Do you want me to come and collect you?'

'No, Helen' he added laughing, 'Guess what? I'm taking the bus. I haven't travelled on one for ages.'

'That's because you no longer enjoy the simple things in life,' Helen said cheerfully, 'however enjoy the trip and I will expect you here, in say an hour's time?'

What would he do, he wondered, if he hadn't Helen. As well as being a first class secretary, Helen was a tall, beautiful woman, with long blonde hair and deep blue eyes. She was a treasure beyond compare, and his workload had decreased considerably since she started work as his personal secretary, three years ago.

John found that although he was very much attracted to her, he had sworn years ago never to have anything to do with women – ever again. He couldn't take that chance of getting hurt again. The hurt that came from his first and only romance was still too fresh in his mind.

It began to rain heavily as he waited for the bus to arrive and when it did, he boarded and took his seat. He was beginning to curse his foolishness in not taking a taxi because his clothes were now soaking wet. The bus was already moving, so he decided to get off at the next stop and make his way home for a change of clothes, using a taxi. Ringing Helen, he told her of his intentions.

'Okay John,' she said happily. 'See you soon!'

At the next bus stop John got ready to disembark, when he observed a young black-haired, blue-eyed woman, who looked so much like his ex-girlfriend of many years ago, a girl called Mary Gallagher. Mary had become for him an unpleasant memory, that he had tried hard over the years to forget. He definitely didn't need reminding that she had almost destroyed him.

In those days, John could never envisage his life without Mary by his side. They were so much in love and were even planning on going to university together in the fall. It was a mutual decision to wait until their university days were over before making their relationship more permanent. They were happy just being together. It's amazing, he thought, how naïve he was at that time.

One day, out of the blue, Mary had ended their relationship and shortly after left Ireland to live with her aunt in Scotland. He never heard from her again. John still felt the anger surge up in him as he recalled that Mary had offered him no explanation as to why. She had ended their relationship so cruelly and, most hurtful of all was that the bad news, in a hand-written note, was delivered by her best friend, Anne Benson. It almost broke John's heart as he read the note over and over again. In the weeks that followed he had tried desperately to see her to find out just what it was he had done that was so wrong. Maybe, he always reasoned, if he could have talked to her and found out the reason why, he could have accepted their break-up more easily.

In his desperation to find out why, he spent most of his time hanging around her house in the hope that he would get to see her. One day her father had come out and angrily warned him to stay away.

'Mary doesn't want to see you,' he roared into John's face. 'Can't you get that into your thick head?'

Scared and embarrassed by the angry reaction from Mary's father, John had walked away without looking back. Mary's rejection of him had hurt him very deeply, and he vowed that no woman would ever be allowed to do that to him again. He had, in spite of his vow, wept bitterly when she left to live in Scotland.

Emotions that John had kept buried this many years surfaced anew in his mind. He was breaking a promise to himself never to think of Mary ever again. Now he was powerless to stop this process of recall once it had started.

'Why,' he asked himself, 'have these thoughts come into my mind at this time?'

He had never married, refusing to let any woman get that close or become part of his life again. At times though, he would often admit to himself that without a woman in his life, he had become a very lonely man.

John was still amazed at the uncanny resemblance this girl had to Mary. He became so curious that he just had to speak to her.

'Excuse me,' he began, 'Sorry to disturb you, but can I ask you a silly question?'

The young woman stared at him, and then as if she realised he was harmless said 'How can I help you?'

'I used to know a girl from around here called Mary Gallagher. You remind me so much of her,' John continued. 'And many years ago she went with her family to live in Scotland.'

'Who wants to know?' asked the woman quietly.

'Sorry,' said John introducing himself, 'I used to go out with Mary before she left for Scotland."

'If we are talking about the same Mary, then I'm Mary's niece. I'm Susan Conway, and I'm over here on a visit with Mary's family. They returned from Scotland just over a year ago.'

Trying to quell the rising excitement in his voice, John asked, "Is Mary home too?'

At first he thought that Susan was ignoring his question and then she said, 'John, I get off at this next stop, there is a café near there and we can talk better there. Will you come with me?'

Standing up, Susan didn't wait for him to answer and left the bus. John, his heart beating rapidly, realised he had no option but to follow her. He needed to know the answers to his many questions.

They went straight to the café and inside Susan went to sit at the table by the window while John went to order their coffees. He came back to where she was sitting, carrying with him two cappuccinos. As he drew near their table, John became very alarmed when he saw that Susan was crying.

Sitting down he asked softly 'Susan, is something wrong? Why are you crying?'

'John there is no other way I can tell you this that will make it easier for you,' she said. 'I know now that you never heard the terrible news about Mary. So you must prepare yourself for a terrible shock.'

For a moment Susan became silent as if she was unable to continue, then speaking ever so softly she added. 'John, Mary died some sixteen years ago in Scotland.'

John felt his body go numb and was glad that he was sitting down.

'Mary was very ill with a cancer,' continued Susan, 'and we all had to accept that she was never going to get well.'

'Cancer,' he said incredulously. 'Surely Mary would have told me.'

'Mary had made a decision, John, to keep this dreadful news within her immediate family.'

'Mary should have told me!' said John remorsefully, 'I should have been told.'

'Our mother spoke many times to Mary about telling you the truth, but she always decided against it. In her own way, John, Mary was only trying to spare you any hurt.'

John felt the tears arrive, and felt Susan's soft hand reach for his in her bid to comfort him. However, he could not be comforted until his body ejected the bitter poison that had built up in him over the last twenty lonely years. Always his mind had been seeking answers, to explain what he had done that was so awful. Now, he knew the truth.

Gradually the time of tears passed, and John regained his composure. Mary had by keeping her condition a secret from him, robbed him of what could have been a special time for them both. However, it took twenty years before he knew the truth, and to learn only today that his Mary was dead had been devastating news to hear.

Her family should have gotten word to him when she had passed. In the end though, it made no difference now, but it would have been nice to have been kept informed and not to have been dismissed so causally.

'What's done is done,' he told himself, silently, 'no use dwelling on past hurts.'

Admitting this, John felt as if a great weight was taken off his shoulders, and suddenly he felt free of all the guilt that he had placed on himself over the years.

'You loved her very much John, didn't you?' Susan's voice bringing him grudgingly back to the present.

'Yes, I did!' answered John. 'I often wondered what I had done to cause Mary and me to part, Susan. I blamed myself but couldn't figure out any reason she had for leaving me.'

'What she did was wrong; John, but she did love you dearly.'

'That I can now accept, Susan.'

Soon it was time for them to leave.

"Isn't it wonderful how we happened to meet this morning, John?"

asked a smiling Susan. 'I guess Mary in some way arranged this to help you achieve closure.'

"Who is to know Susan?" said John 'Who can say different?'

'What are your plans now John?' asked Susan

'I guess it is time for me to get on with my life, Susan,' he replied.

'Good luck John,' said Susan. 'I wish you well for the future.' With that she grabbed her purse and left the café.

John sat back in his chair and his thoughts were about Mary and how she had tried to shield him from the knowledge of her having a fatal cancer. John didn't blame Mary in any way. However, he was sorry that Mary in her wisdom thought he needed shielding from bad news. If he had been told what was wrong, he knew in his heart he would have wanted to have been there for her – every step of the way.

As he left the café, John felt free and happier than he had been for a long time. As he sat waiting on his taxi to arrive, his mind could only think of Helen, working diligently away at his furniture store. He had been often tempted to ask her out on a date and now, he thought to himself, if she accepted, dinner at the Savoy hotel tonight for the two of them would be a great way to begin.

Tony Lafferty is from Strabane, Co. Tyrone. This is his first time to be published in the Ireland's Own Anthology of Winning Short Stories.

Making and Mending

BY MARY SHIEL

*In the short space of two generations, values have changed so much
that our old self-sufficient frugal world is now quite extinct.*

'A STITCH IN TIME saves nine' and 'waste not, want not'
were two of my mother's favourite maxims. Not surprising
really, coming as she did from a large working class family,
where self-sufficiency was a necessity. She and her sisters made all
their own clothes.

They knitted jumpers, cardigans and even their brothers' socks.
They were skilled leather workers and milliners, producing handbags,
gloves and hats of high quality. Nor were her brothers idle; they
could, and did, repair the family's boots and shoes and mended
broken items of furniture.

Naturally my mother carried her talents into married life, and as
she had six children, sewing and knitting for them occupied all her
free time. She was widowed young, and the most stringent economies
were needed to keep us fed and dressed. Every cast-off garment of
her sisters was painstakingly unpicked, turned and remade. Jumpers
were ripped and the wool recycled. Being the eldest, I was enlisted at
an early age as Mam's right hand woman in the struggle to keep the
family clad.

Having been cut from the same piece of cloth as my mother and
aunts, I found all this activity enjoyable. So much so, that I kept it on
after starting work. In any case, most girls seemed to make at least
some of their own clothes, and Dublin abounded in shops selling
materials, patterns and haberdashery of an Aladdin's Cave variety.

Marriage and four children kept my husband and me 'making and mending', as a popular radio programme of the time was called. Unless they were teachers or nurses, women were obliged to give up their jobs once they got married, and had to use their housekeeping allowances wisely. To be respected as a good provider and homemaker was essential to a woman's self worth in an era when she was unlikely to have any other career.

Today, I see my daughters and their friends uninterested in crafts of any kind. Even simple tasks are beyond them. Garments are discarded for want of a button – ripped hems are mended with Sellotape. All this in spite of strenuous efforts on the part of mothers and teachers to inculcate even the most rudimentary skills. Admittedly, the advent of chain stores and boutiques with reasonably priced clothing has removed any real incentive to home dressmaking, as you will readily be told by these same young people!

The same profligate spirit seems to permeate all areas of our much more affluent lives. The yardstick which governed the disposal of my paypacket – a third to my mother, a third saved and a third spent – is as archaic today as not being properly dressed without gloves and a hat. For a large proportion of modern women, homemaking is no longer a priority.

Mostly from necessity, they continue to work after marriage, and convenience is the keynote to their household tasks. Their fulfilment now comes mainly from their jobs, which is a pity for their sakes, as it leaves the creative side of their natures unexplored.

Occasionally one of my mother's mottos such as 'mind the shillings and the pounds will take care of themselves' springs unbidden to my lips, as I listen to some tale of penury from a spendthrift daughter. This is met by blank incomprehension on her part, and the accusation of not understanding anything. I fear she may be right. In the short space of two generations, values have changed so much that our old self-sufficient frugal world is now quite extinct. More and more do I feel like a 'relic of auld decency!'

Mary Sheil is from Drumcondra, Dublin. This is her second successive time to be published in the Ireland's Own Anthology of Winning Short Stories.

The Kerry Set

By Donal A. Buckley

Steve is returning home to his native Kerry after more than forty years working in London, having gone over in search of work like so many others at a time when emigration was rife. He was wondering how he would find things at home after all this time …

STEVE FARLEY sat in the departure lounge at Gatwick Airport waiting to board a flight back to his native Kerry. He left his rural home in his early twenties to seek a job in England. But that was over forty years ago, at a time when emigration was rife in Ireland. Steve recalled the day he left on a bus destined for Cork City and then on a train to Rosslare Harbour to board the ferry to Fishguard.

When he disembarked the sky was dark and grey. Pouring rain sent water gushing down from the hills overlooking the harbour. A train was waiting on the platform to transport him and other passengers to Paddington Station in London. He had a friend's address in Harlesden, tucked carefully in the inside pocket of his jacket. After alighting from the train, he hailed a taxi to the address on the High Street. He rang the door-bell and knocked on the door but there was no reply. Just as he was about to walk away, a woman with red hair and a blue spotted apron opened the door.

'Are you Steve?' she asked.

The taxi driver brought his bag up to the front door and he paid the fare.

'Come on in', she said. They shook hands and he followed her up a narrow stairs and into the living room. A man was stretched on the floor snoring.

'There's your friend Tommy. He's full-up with drink. Close the door and I'll make you a bite to eat after your journey all the way from Kerry. Tommy will wake up in a few hours and he'll probably give you a start in the morning,' she told him.

'Getting the start' was the main concern for Irish emigrants, but Steve was lucky that his friend Tommy Fitzgerald was a Ganger with one of the largest building construction firms in London. On his first morning, he watched in dismay as men were lined up to be selected for work. There was no shovel and pickaxe for him, he was given a time sheet and record book for over one hundred men, with strict instructions to instantly fire any man not performing or slacking back on the job.

He suffered extreme loneliness and culture shock that never really subsided during his long, enforced working life in England. He often had to endure hard physical labour and lived in rough accommodation until he got a job as a London bus driver.

But now he was on his first visit home to Ireland in over forty years. He wondered would his brother recognise him when he stepped off the plane. Steve never married, although he loved dancing at the Irish clubs in London. He lived a good social life with his friends. He was shocked and taken aback by the drunkenness and behaviour of the labouring workers.

As he queued at the departure gate, he also wondered should he be returning at all. He had not even returned home when his mother died!

Steve remembered the morning he left his home. His mother was crying; she knew she would never see him again. His father had died when a bull gored him in the yard of the family farm. The night before he left, he said goodbye to a neighbour's daughter that he often danced with in the local hall. She was now married to a local butcher with a grown-up family. As he handed over his boarding card something inside him told him he'd never return to London again.

This day was worth waiting for, after a lifetime away from his roots in his native Kerry. As the plane took off, he watched the disappearing

English countryside far below and looked forward to seeing the first glimpse of his island home. His pulse quickened as the east coast of Ireland came into view. This was the moment he had waited for since the day he first set foot on English soil.

When he walked out at the airport arrivals' hall, his brother Jack and two sons were there to meet him. He threw his arms around his brother and shook hands with the nephews he had never met. When they arrived at the home place, he viewed the old stone-built farm buildings.

They looked just the same as the day he left. He often bagged grain into the loft after a threshing and turned the cows into their stalls for milking. The swallows still nested in the high walls of the old forge. The dairy, where in his childhood he often turned the handle of the milk separator for his mother while he watched the cream slowly flowing into an enamelled jug for butter making, is now the nerve centre for the family's robotic milking system.

His brother's tractor and combine-harvester were parked in the old horse stable. The dwelling house, with its domed glass porch and tall chimney, didn't appear to have changed much, but the concrete coated yard and new milking parlour, transformed the farm into a modern holding.

'Come on in, we have a little surprise for you,' his brother said. When he entered the house, the large living room was filled with his surviving friends and neighbours, waiting to welcome home the returned emigrant. Jack's wife, Mary Anne, and local women served a welcome meal with drinks and stories of past years easing the return home for Steve. He chatted to his old school friend Johnny Meade, about his exploits delivering the post in the locality.

'Would you like another cup of tea?' a woman asked from behind Steve's shoulder? He turned quickly to the sound of a very familiar voice. He looked up at the two bright eyes and broad smile of his former dancing partner, Madge Griffin. She quickly placed the tea-pot on the table and placed her two arms tight around his broad shoulders.

'I've waited for this day for a long time,' she said.

He was speechless, as she sat down beside him at the table. Madge told him her life's story. A few years after he left, she married Mick O'Dea, the local butcher. They had two sons now in Australia and a daughter married to a Guard in Longford.

'How is Mick?' Steve asked.

'The marriage broke up a long time ago. He remarried and moved up the country with his new wife. I was left to rear and educate the children. I opened a hairdressing saloon in the town and made a new life for myself,' she told him.

'Are you going to dance with me again?' she asked with a roguish smile. 'You were a great dancer!' she exclaimed.

After the meal the large dining room table was pushed to one side and Mick Randles reached for his accordion and started playing.

'Come on Steve, we'll lead the floor,' Madge suggested.

'It's a long time since I danced a Kerry Set' he said.

It wasn't long before the floor was full with dancers and merriment filled the air, as Steve tried to remember the steps and moves to the amusement of his partner and neighbours. 'You did very well,' she told him, as he sat beside her on a large couch.

'I'm going to take you out for a drive and a meal at one of our best hotels on Saturday evening. I'm sure we'll have a lot to talk about old times,' she told him. The celebrations continued until the early hours before she left for home.

On the Saturday evening, Steve and Madge enjoyed a meal of fresh river salmon at a lake hotel. They reminisced about their dancing days in the local hall.

'Do you remember the night you sat on the crossbar of my bicycle and we nearly drove straight into the path of the parish priest's Morris Minor car on our way home from a football match?' Steve asked.

Madge laughed, as they adjourned to the lounge for coffee and to view the lake and mountains in the evening sunset. Steve moved to the window to see two boats with fishermen casting their rods in search of brown trout.

'Would you like to be out on the lake fishing?' she asked.

'I was never a good fisherman. I loved playing football with the home team, but all that finished when I went to England in search of work,' he replied.

'Tell me about your time in London,' she asked.

Steve reached for the coffee pot and refilled his cup. 'I love a good cup of strong coffee,' he remarked. Madge was still sipping a glass of red wine, as she probed into Steve's life across the water.

'I was just twenty-three years of age when I received the call from Tommy Fitzgerald to come over and work on the buildings in London. I had no idea what life would be like and where I was going to live. When I arrived, Tommy's wife Kate had a spare room in the house and I had a roof over my head for the first few months.

'Then Tommy was moved to another part of London and I lost my abode and the bit of security. I made a few pounds to tide me over until I moved into a one-roomed flat. The hours were long, but the money was good. I was never a drinker or gambler and after a number of years, I applied for a job as a London bus driver.

'I had to attend an intensive training course and driving test. I got the job and that day dramatically changed my life. After about ten years driving, I was promoted to Inspector and I retired a few weeks ago as Manager of a large bus depot in the city.

'I made many friends from all over Ireland who danced in the Irish Clubs to the famous Irish showbands and Céilí bands. I played some football with the lads working in London.

'Then, a telegram arrived to say my mother had died. For some untold reason I never crossed the Irish Sea to attend her funeral. To this day, my brother and sisters still complain that I left the family down. But time is a great healer. They were all present to welcome me home on Tuesday night. My sister, Josie, took me to visit her grave.

'She was a wonderful woman to rear five children after my father died. A Hereford bull gored him in the yard on a sunny Sunday when I was just seven years of age.

The old school building is still standing but the local creamery is a thing of the past, I've noticed,' he told her.

'Was there no woman in your life after all your years in London and when do you plan to return?' Madge enquired.

Steve put his hand into one of his jacket pockets and placed a small silver box on the table.

'I have something very special for you,' he said. 'Some weeks before I got the call to travel to London all those years ago, I visited a jewellers shop in Tralee. I had planned to ask you to marry me and I kept the ring safe in the hope that some day we may meet again.'

Madge's eyes were glued to the little box resting on the table. 'Are you going open the box?' she asked.

Steve smiled, as he released the clasp to raise the cover. She watched, as he held a gold engagement ring with a glistening diamond in his hand.

'Is this for me?' she gasped.

He slipped the ring on to her finger and the diamond sparkled in the evening sun. He walked to the bar and a waiter returned with two glasses of champagne. Their glasses touched, as she gazed at the ring on her finger and admired the silver-haired man sitting beside her on the leather couch.

Donal A. Buckley is from Silverspring, Cork City. This is his second time to be published in the Ireland's Own Anthology of Winning Short Stories. *He was published also in 2013.*

The Cauldron of Plenty

By Linda Guerin

Fish and chips takeaways were popular in the 1960s as now, but Dad had a different treat in mind on the memorable night he brought me with him for the first time.

IN THE 1960s, Limerick people on their way home from pubs and cinemas could purchase fish and chips, burgers and a lots of other fast food from a range of modern, brightly-lit, takeaway restaurants. Whenever my parents could afford it, they liked to have a Saturday night treat of fish and chips.

Usually my father would put on his overcoat around ten o'clock and head off for the nearest takeaway. I remember one time my father invited me to go with him. I was about six or seven at the time and I was excited at the prospect of being out late at night. I put on my coat, hat and gloves and stepped out into the chilly autumnal air. My warm breath condensed into a white mist as I walked along the dark street with my father.

It had been raining earlier in the evening and pools of rainwater had collected in hollows on the roads and dips in the footpaths. Their silvery surfaces shimmered in a light breeze and reflected shop fronts, passers-by and cars. In a few minutes we reached a fish and chips shop.

The aroma of its deep-fat fried food escaped from the premises as customers went in and out. I expected us to stop, push the glass door open and join the queue at the high counter, but my father walked on. Puzzled, I followed him for a while until he came to a halt at the entrance to a small shop. Then he went inside.

There were about six to eight people in wet overcoats ahead of us in the softly-lit interior. We all stood in a narrow corridor that ran

146

along the side of a waist-high counter. I had assumed that my father had set out to buy a fish and chips takeaway for the family. However, there was no sign of crispy chips arranged in small white bags or no hint of sizzling battered cod cooking in a stainless steel deep-fat fryer.

As I looked around, a lady approached the counter and addressed us cheerfully, 'It'll be another twenty minutes.' Everyone nodded their heads and lapsed into muted conversations, their murmured whisperings mixed with the beating of the rain against the big, front window and the tap-tap of raindrops as they were blown in by the wind through the entrance to the shop.

A short time later more people arrived in from the dark street, swelling the number of patrons waiting patiently in the narrow corridor. The lady reiterated her message. 'It'll be another twenty minutes.' But what were we all waiting for?

Then, the lady opened the connecting door between the shop and the kitchen at the rear of the premises. Immediately a blast of warm, steamy air gained admittance to the cold, damp shop, carrying with it the mouth-watering aroma of what I guessed might be cooked pork.

At that moment I caught sight for the first time of a large, shining cauldron as it sat on top of a stove. It reminded me of the Cauldron of Plenty that belonged to the Dagda, the Celtic god in Irish mythology. I had been reading about him and his cauldron in a library book. According to tradition no one ever left the magic cooking pot hungry and it was believed that the Dagda's cauldron never ran dry.

As I watched wisps of steam escape from the edge of the lid, I thought of the Bronze Age hunter-gatherer peoples who told stories of the Dagda long ago. They would crowd around fires and watch cooking pots in the evenings, hoping to satisfy their hunger, nourish their spirits and share a feast with family and friends. Since then human beings have acquired new fashions, new forms of transportation and new technology, but their basic needs have stayed the same.

Then, the wait was over. In the subdued atmosphere of the shop people muttered their orders. The lady left for the kitchen and half-closed the connecting door behind her so I could not see her lift the lid of the cauldron and dole out its contents.

Soon, the door opened again and white-paper parcels were put on the counter. Customers handed over notes and coins and received their change. Now it was my father's turn. He smiled as he placed an order for pig's toes.

A few minutes later we were out in the dark street. I had been put in charge of the big, white-paper parcel which was steaming gently in the cold, night air. When we arrived home, my mother unwrapped the parcel and placed the crubeens, the Irish word for pig's toes, on plates.

The crubeens had a tasty, fatty flavour that reminded me of bacon. Then we polished them off with cups of tea. Even our cat had a takeaway. She devoured the scraps and spent the remainder of the evening licking her lips, cleaning her face and washing her paws.

For some reason that night my father had gone in search of more traditional fare than fish and chips. He had hungered for crubeens, a takeaway which might have been more plentiful when he was a boy.

Linda Guerin is from St. Patrick's Road, Limerick. This is her third time to be published in the Ireland's Own Anthology of Winning Short Stories. *She was overall winner in 2013.*

A Bit of Light

By Anne Walsh Donnelly

*Since the loss of her husband she is often in conversation with her statue
of the Angel Gabriel; she misses Paddy terribly and is contemplating
joining him. But daughter Sharon is having a hard time too with
her newborn baby and she needs help …*

I DON'T HEAR any birds this morning. That's good. I wouldn't
want to die on a day that might be full of the voices of wrens or
cuckoos or thrushes. Mulligan's rooster starts to crow - never a
need for an alarm clock in our village.

I don't know what I want for breakfast. I might have one of those
croissants I got in Tesco yesterday. Not great for the cholesterol but
that hardly matters now. The kitchen window blind creaks as I pull it
up. Grey clouds dress the sky. The willow that Paddy planted on our
twenty-fifth wedding anniversary is flailing in the wind.

As I'm waiting for the kettle to boil the angel Gabriel glares at me.

'Are you going to light my candle?' he asks.

'Are you going to let me see him again?'

'You will, in time.'

'Yeah, but not on this earth,' I say, as I grab a cup from the shelf.

He can be awful annoying at times. He's been standing on the
window-sill since Paddy's funeral and at first I used to light the candle
that he holds in his porcelain hands.

'A bit of light in the darkness,' said my sister, when she gave the
angel to me.

A fire hazard more like; I've often been in the car on the way to
town and I'd remember that I forgot to blow the bloody candle out.

149

I'd have to come home again, 'cos there was one time that I did forget. No use in having a bit of light in the darkness when your whole house is gone up in flames, is there?'

'I'm not going to light your candle,' I say as I rinse my cup with some boiling water. My cheeks feel flushed and damp from the steam so I grab the tea towel and sponge my face.

Then I think of the red cheeks on Paddy and his bulging eyes when he'd get cross. It's easier to think of that, than his happy face. I mightn't miss him as much if he was one of those husbands who spent half the night slobbering over a pint in the pub, or worse slobbering over some young one half his age. Or his passing might be a bit easier to bear if he took a fist to me once in a while and I hated the living sight of him.

But I loved every bit of the man, the feel of the hairs on his back as we made love, the grassy smell of him after he'd come in from cutting the silage, the heat of his hand on my thigh as we sat watching the Nine O'Clock news on the couch. All the coal I heap into the stove does nothing for me now and I can't even get warm in the bed. Despite the electric blanket, hot water bottle and winter duvet there's a chill in my bones that I can't get rid of.

I clench my fingers around the handle of the cup.

'You've no idea what it's like to lose your husband.'

'You're right, I don't,' says Gabriel.

'Well, the least you could do is be a bit sympathetic.'

I managed to get through Paddy's funeral 'cos I'd planned what I was going to do once it was over. But my problem is that sometimes I find it hard to keep my mouth shut so didn't I go tell my sister what was going through my head. The next thing I know, Doctor McCarthy is in the house and Paddy's coffin still in the front room. Whatever was in the injection he bruised my bum cheek with, it knocked all thoughts of going to the river out of my head for a while. Then after the injection he put me on the Xanax.

'They'll keep you on an even keel,' he said.

I stopped taking them, weeks ago. Couldn't fit into any of my clothes and I was walking around in a daze the whole time.

There's a text message from Sharon waiting for me when I turn on the phone.

'Mam r u at home?'

'Where else would I be?'

'You'd better text her back,' says Gabriel.

'Not today.'

I grab a spoon and squeeze the life out of the tea bag that I've just dumped into my cup. As I lighten the tea with some milk, Gabriel starts nattering again.

'You could do with some company.'

'It's not Sharon that I want to talk to.'

Anyway, it wouldn't be fair on Sharon if I was to see her this morning 'cos I'd hate the thought of her at my funeral, turning today over and over in her head blaming herself; was there something she didn't pick up on. 'Cos this isn't about her and there's nothing she can do anyway. Grief is a solitary thing. I read that some where, and I've never read a truer word.

Anyway she has enough on her hands at the moment looking after Tommy.

'Well, maybe Sharon might want to see you,' says Gabriel.

'She doesn't need me. She has her own family now.'

'Paddy wouldn't like what you're planning.'

'You have no idea what he'd like.'

I throw the tea towel over Gabriel's head. That'll take the shine off his face and maybe give me a bit of peace as well. Then I take my tea and croissant and sit on the chair furthest away from the kitchen window.

I'm just about to take a drink when the back door bursts open. In walks Sharon lugging Tommy's car seat and he's bawling his head off. Jesus, he can roar for a three-month-old. The thin screech in his cry nearly cuts my heart in two and turns my thoughts to the brandy I used to put in Sharon's bottle when she was the same way. But she breast feeds. Maybe I should give the brandy to her instead.

I heard on the radio recently that they don't put alcohol in gripe water anymore so that's not going to do much good. You'd think by now that someone would have invented an App for the phone that could cure a colicky baby. An App like that would make you a millionaire.

Every bit of Sharon's body is drooping. She heaves the car seat onto the table and flops into a chair.

'Colic?'

'That's what the doctor keeps telling me,' she says, as she fumbles with the buckle and extracts Tommy. The poor little mite's body is shaking and his bib is soaked. His fist connects with her eye and now the two of them are roaring their heads off.

I take Tommy and rest his shaking head on my shoulder. My navy dress will be destroyed with his dribble but sure what harm, he's stopped crying.

'Drink that,' I say to her, pointing at my tea.

She drains the cup, then bites into my croissant and demolishes the whole lot of it.

'I feel like a failure,' she says, between sobs, as she wipes the greasy pastry from her lips.

'Every new mother feels that way, it will get better, pet.'

'The minute you take him, he stops crying, how the hell do you do that?'

'Maybe it's his way of telling you to go have a rest.'

She has the look now that she used to have as a child when she'd pick the 'Get out of Jail Free Card,' in Monopoly. Then I think of the neat pile of Xanax waiting for me upstairs in the drawer of my bedside locker. Tommy moves his head a bit on my shoulder so I get up and walk around the kitchen and rub his back to soothe him to sleep.

'I've expressed some milk, could you take him … for a small while?'

I hide the feeling of panic that's creeping through me. I've never minded Tommy before. It would be too much trouble, she'd say when I used to offer, what with her breastfeeding and all.

I stare at the shrouded Gabriel on the window-sill, picturing the smug grin he's probably wearing on his devout face.

'Is this your way of ruining my plans?'

And even the tea towel doesn't prevent him from answering back.

'Sharon needs you.'

'I was supposed to be going out with some of the women from the active retirement group today,' I say to Sharon, watching the convulsive dance her feet are doing under the table.

'Do you have to go?'

I close my eyes for a minute and sink my face into the crook of Tommy's neck. He smells of talcum powder. Wish I could bottle it and keep it on my bedside locker. It might be better than a pile of pills.

The chair scrapes the kitchen tiles as Sharon stands. Then she's beside me and I open my eyes. There's a tremor in her hands as she turns the tap to rinse the cup. The haggard look on her face makes me want to hug her but I don't want to put Tommy down for fear he'll wake. I glance sideways at Gabriel. Then I turn back to look at Sharon and attempt a smile.

'I don't have to go. Sure, I'll have much better fun here with Tommy.'

'Thanks, Mam.'

Almost as soon as she's gone Tommy wakes, which is just as well as my shoulder is killing me. I put him back in his car seat and nuke the expressed milk in the microwave. If Sharon saw me she'd probably combust but I haven't the energy to put it in the bottle warmer she left behind. And by the sounds of it I don't think poor Tommy has the patience to wait.

When the bottle's ready I take him out of his car seat, sit on Paddy's rocking chair by the range. He closes his eyes and sucks on the teat. When the milk is gone, he burps the same way Paddy used to after a feed of steak and onions. Then came an almighty whiff and a look of pure relief on his face.

I get up with him still in my arms and push the kitchen window open to let in some fresh air. At least Paddy never deteriorated to the stage where I would end up cleaning his behind. Tommy's face is alight now and a warm feeling spreads all over my body. Paddy is looking straight out of Tommy's brown eyes.

A gust of wind blows the tea towel from Gabriel's face onto the worktop.

'You brought him back to me.'

As soon as Tommy's changed, he falls asleep and I put him into his car seat. I don't want him to get a cold from the draught so I close the window but knock Gabriel over in the process. I pick him up and examine him for cracks. Thankfully there's none.

But if I didn't know any better I'd swear there's a tear on his cheek. But angels don't cry, do they? Still, he looks cold so after I put him back on the window-sill, I light his candle. And as I blow out the match an amber hue travels up his chest and lands on his pale face.

Anne Walsh Donnelly is from Castlebar, Co. Mayo. This is her second time to be published in the Ireland's Own Anthology of Winning Short Stories. *She was a runner-up in the Beginners' short story category last year.*

Once Upon A Christmastime

By John T. Martin

Harking back to the Christmas time of youth, long before the internet or even television existed in our homes; no iPads, no X Boxes, no DVDs. It was a time from another age, a moment from another world …

IT WAS A TIME long, long before the Celtic Tiger seductively purred in the undergrowth. It was even a time before the Rural Electrification Scheme poured its glaring light into the dark solitude of the Irish rural countryside, chasing away the mystery and magic of flickering firelight, dancing shadows and the rituals associated with the lighting of oil lamps and candles. It seems such a long time ago, yet less than a lifetime has passed.

It was a time when Christmas decorations, stored in a battered, rusting biscuit tin, were revived from their annual hibernation. Colourful paper streamers stretched like elongated accordions, festooning the low ceilings with their thumb tacked glory.

Pride of place was given to the tree, the top of a young spruce, standing in the corner in all its splendour. Clip-on candleholders perched precariously on the ends of branches, the tiny red spiralled candles bravely and dangerously flickering among the delicate colour-ed glass baubles hung on scraps of thread.

A length of string necklaced the chimney breast, supporting the handful of Christmas cards. Sprigs of holly sprouted from behind the picture of the Sacred Heart, the red berries glistening like drops of blood. From the battery powered wireless perched on the window sill, Bing Crosby dreamily crooned his eternal vision of a White Christmas.

Once the Feast of the Immaculate Conception on the 8th of December was past, the countdown began in earnest. Homework was completed with diligence, bedtimes adhered to without complaint, everyone on their very best behaviour in case Santy got wind of even the tiniest indiscretion. Then, at last, the day arrived, the wait was finally over.

It was a time when Christmas Eve seemed unending, the giddiness of anticipation almost unbearable. It was a day of severe fast and abstinence, 'A Famine before a Feast,' we were told, the penance exacerbated by the smell of the ham, glazed with sugar and dotted with cloves, spitting and sizzling in the oven of the solid fuel cooker, powered by turf that had been hand won from the summer bog.

At last, blissful darkness, and the placing of the tall red candle in the window to guide the Holy Family should they happen to find themselves wandering the back roads of the remote Irish countryside on this most precious night. As always, the lighting of the candle carried out with great ceremony, the honour of putting match to wick falling to the youngest member of the household.

Memories crowd in of walking the mile and a half to Midnight Mass, the church ablaze with candlelight and the fragrance of incense carried aloft on its smoke high into the rafters. The lulling cadence of the Latin Mass contributing to the magical atmosphere and providing an affirmation that this was the night on which the Saviour was born and that all would be right with the world.

The choir rising to the occasion, 'Silent Night, Holy Night,' and it was both. After Mass a quick visit to the crib. The holy family, with the baby in the centre, surrounded by plaster shepherds kneeling on Mick McGrath's straw. The hurried rush home, slipping and sliding on the ice sheathed puddles, keeping a watchful eye skywards, fearful that Santy would be ahead of schedule.

Breaking the fast with mugs of hot tea and doorstep sandwiches with generous helpings of the freshly cooked Christmas ham embedded between thick slices of liberally buttered shop batch bread, a special treat.

Then time for bed. Covers pulled up over tousled heads for fear that a glimpse of the great man might cause him to disappear, never to return. Tossing and turning for what seemed like hours, no memory of falling asleep.

And then, morning dawned.

Excited yelps and yells as the parcels at the end of the bed were torn apart to reveal their meagre contents. The "Dandy Annual," with Desperate Dan on the cover tucking into his favourite Cow Pie with the horns sticking out through the crust; a box of lead soldiers, resplendent in their scarlet tunics and black busbys, a set of timber building blocks, made in China, with instructions in a quaint version of English.

And wonder of wonders, a clockwork train set, constrained to run its endless course on the tiny circular track, round and round, round and round!

Once upon a Christmastime, long before the internet or even television existed in our homes. No iPads, no X Boxes, no DVDs, it was a time from another age, a moment from another world. It was a difficult time, a time of severe scarcity and simple pleasures provided by board games like Snakes and Ladders and Ludo, and card games such as Snap and 'Beggar my Neighbour.' But above all it was a time imbued with innocence and a richness of spirit that can never be replicated.

John. T. Martin is from Kilcullen, Co. Kildare. This is his second time to be published in the Ireland's Own Anthology of Winning Short Stories. *He was published also in the 2012 edition.*

A shilling for the Child of Prague

By Paul McLaughlin

*Little Mary, in the absence of her mother, lives with her grandmother
in a crowded Belfast street, and Granny had lots of superstitions
and her own peculiar ways …*

'MINNIE REA, Minnie Rea, her Mammy's run away hey', ran the words with the rhythm of the turning rope, as the skipping song rang out across the street. A makeshift choir of urchins in torn frocks and plastic sandals twirled and reeled to the music of flat accents, with mocking faces that wore laughter like macabre masks. And every girl-child took her place in a row of ridicule that laughed with scorn up towards Minnie Rea's face framed in her bedroom window.

The rest of Belfast's Cargan Street went about its business as if nothing was amiss. Mrs McFarland cardinal-polished her step at number 26, hunched over and puffing a Park Drive in time with her rubbing, back and forth, back and forth, puff, breath, puff, breath.

Old Mister Grant, straight-backed on a kitchen chair outside number 30, read his morning newspaper, collarless and shoeless, bringing it back and forth into view like the slide of a trombone, while Paddy O'Brien, the bread server, bellowed the sweet smell of freshly baked bread into the Summer air as, in turn, he inserted and extracted his long tray pole into and out of the back of his bakery van.

Only Mary Elizabeth Rea, still as a little statue behind the starched, white, net curtain of her bedroom at number 27, recognised the spite in those young voices and winced as it cut her to the quick. She stood frightened and hurt in her anger waiting for the circle of the spell to break.

'Mary Elizabeth', called her grandmother from the bottom of the stairs: 'Run down to Hillis' shop for a rabbit and no dallying. A dilatory girl will find no comfort in dawdling.'

Minnie grimaced at the formality of her full name and then smiled for the first time that day at her grandmother's fine words. Old Maggie Rea was the lady of the street all right, everyone said so. She had never darkened the door of a mill or the wrong side of a shop counter, they said. And all her big words came from the house on the hill in the country where she had been born and raised.

'Dilatory, indeed. Who else but Grannie Rea would have known, never mind used that word in these parts?' And Minnie's voice was a tiny echo on the high-ceilinged landing as she slipped past an opened window and the continuing chorus of chants and squeals before meeting her grandmother on the stairs.

'Don't pass me, girl, you know it's unlucky. Quick, go down to the scullery, the sixpence for the dinner is beside the jaw box.'

Minnie waited while her grandmother, the high neck of her collar stiff, white and unrelenting against the blackness of her bodice, climbed to the back bedroom for her afternoon nap. 'A lady must have her rest everyday if she is going to look her best,' the old woman said to herself, as she fingered her tortoiseshell Rosary.

'When the good Lord made bed, he made the best thing of all.' And with that, her usual mantra, the bedroom door was pulled tight shut and the key turned with a ring of finality.

Every day, at exactly two o'clock, Maggie took to her bed. Three hours later, she would descend, 'physically and spiritually revived', she said, with a fresh glow to her cheeks and the perfume of sloes on her breath.

Her 'special time', she called it, although her secret had long been shared by the twelve-year-old Minnie whose childish dalliances with the ladies at the dock gates had familiarised her with the smell of gin. She loved their painted smiles and kohl-tinted eyes and knew that their cigarette-cracked voices held a laughter that was as warm as their hearts. They called her their little sweetheart and pressed pennies into her hands for the many errands she ran to Duignan's tobacconists.

Minnie thought of them often and always as her friends. She had said as much to her skipping partners only the previous night and had soon realised her mistake. They had laughed and mocked in equal measure and Minnie had run home with their shrieks of abuse ringing in her ears.

'Never tell anyone what you think or feel, especially not what you feel,' she thought: 'It's like Father McGarry says, your one true friend is the Sacred Heart!'

Mary blessed herself, saying the words slowly and sincerely, grabbed the sixpence from the worktop and slipped the latch off the backdoor before stepping into the yard. Masses of nasturtiums, like the welcoming flames of Hell in her 'Illustrated Catechism', danced against the whitewashed walls, jostling and shoving to reach the thin shafts of sunlight that brought heat and growth.

They were fierce on the eye and gentle to the touch and Minnie squinted and caressed them for the living things they were. Her grandmother planted great pots of nasturtiums each year after Easter and awaited their 'resurrection', as she called it, anointing them from an old teapot filled with a Co. Tyrone recipe of herbs and water that made them grow as big as sunflowers. They filled the yard with the smell of summer in Dromore, her grandmother said, 'a scent to take the filth of the city from your nostrils'.

Minnie unbolted the yard door and stepped gingerly into the entry, looking to left and right for any 'traffic of torture' that might come her way, but all was clear as far as the corner and the hundred-yard dash to Hillis' shop.

George Hillis, his long white apron freckled with blood, whipped the rabbit from its hook high above the shop front like a fairground hustler, wrapped it expertly in the remains of yesterday's newspaper and passed it to her gently like a gift. He took the sixpence and gave Minnie a smile and a baritone "thank you". Mister George was a gentleman, a real gentleman and Minnie found it hard to believe that he would burn for eternity just because he was a Protestant. It was another mystery among many others, she thought.

She remembered the tilt of his bowler hat and the strut of his walk as he'd marched proudly down Cargan Street to join the Orange parade the past Twelfth of July. The navy serge suit had been dry cleaned specially and somehow, she thought, he looked like a bridegroom. Or what a bridegroom should look like.

He had passed the time of day with her that morning, 'Hello my little Minnie Mouse' and asked her to pray for a 'good, dry day for the brethren', tipping his hat and blowing her a fragile kiss from a white, gloved palm. Minnie had asked Our Lord for the best of weather for her Protestant friend and, a little surprisingly perhaps, Our Lord had said, 'yes'.

She shook aside her thoughts and returned to the house by her practised route, all the time watching nervously for unwelcome friends in the alley, before setting the rabbit gently in the jaw box. She unwrapped the newspaper, its blurred newsprint clinging equally to fur and hand, and was careful to avoid the dead gaze of the once beautiful eyes. She knew that they would now lie open like little mirrors and she did not want to see her own face staring back at her in accusation.

Grandmother would cut off one of its feet for luck and hang it on the yard wall to ward off evil spirits, as she had done since she was a little girl up the country. But as luck would have it, the fresh rash of orange, red and yellow nasturtiums, with their unparalleled growth, would eventually mask her row of rotting talismans.

Minnie didn't think it right to kill poor animals and had even said so once, but only once. Her grandmother's tongue had forgotten the big house on the hill for a moment and lashed her like Our Lord at the scourging.

'God curse you for an ungrateful child, she had screamed: 'Is it not bad enough that I'm left my leaf-alone to rear you without the bile of your mother rising in your throat to question me. Never cross me again.'

Her mother had been mentioned, damned and forgotten in a volley of words that brooked no questioning. And Minnie had stood silent and ashamed. Always ashamed of the mother she could no longer remember well enough to defend.

No explanations were offered, no words to wipe the slate and not even the sentimental scent of the spirits on her grandmother's goodnight kiss had been enough to break her silence, but little tears, like perfect pearls, had formed in the corners of the old woman's eyes. Then, silence, bed and acceptance.

Minnie quickly tidied away the tea leaves that would make a bed of food for the flowers and dusted and polished the kitchen until even the late July sun could find no telltale particles under his scrutinous eye.

She lifted the statue of the Child of Prague from the window sill and whispered when she found the silver coin underneath. 'Another of grandmother's superstitions,' she said to herself. 'A home with a silver coin under the Boy Christ will never know want'.

She dusted the statue from the little golden cross on its crowned head to the plaque showing the words 'Child of Prague' that fronted its plinth, hugging it to her breast and glancing sideways to the rectangular picture of Our Lady of Perpetual Succour that took pride of place in the room.

'O Holy Mother,' she whispered, holding the child tightly, 'Please ask your dear Son to protect my mother now and at the hour of her death.'

Minnie set the statue, its silver dowry safely filed beneath, square in the window, directly opposite the big brass, striking clock on the mantle, before seeking out the yellowing, white envelope tucked tightly behind it. The letter had sat there for more than five years, for as long as Minnie could remember and longer than she would be able to forget. It was moved only for dusting and replaced immediately afterwards. The letter from her mother, with the Liverpool postmark, that had never been opened.

Mary touched it for luck and for life. A gentle, finger-tipping kind of touch at one of its increasingly frail and fragile corners that offered only the slightest hint of contact where none was permitted. For luck was a shilling under the Child of Prague and life the unread pleading of an absent mother.

Paul McLaughlin is from Marmount Gardens, Belfast. He is a regular contributor to Ireland's Own *magazine and the* Ireland's Own Anthology of Winning Short Stories. *He was overall winner in 2014.*

Rockets and Rossini

By Kevin Lewis

Growing up in Wexford next door to the Theatre Royal fuelled an interest in the many attractions of the annual world famous Opera Festival, on stage and off …

THE ROCKET shot upwards into the night like a comet streaking through the atmosphere, leaving a trail of bright light in its wake and then, reaching the summit of its climb, exploded into myriad kaleidoscopic colours that lit up the sky and fell earthwards like a giant weeping willow, before fizzling out in the drizzly darkness. It was fireworks night and the annual Wexford Opera Festival had begun.

As a young boy in Wexford during the early sixties this night in October was always one to remember. The Wexford Opera Festival had been founded in 1951 by Dr. Tom Walsh, together with a few of his close friends who shared his love of this art form.

For two weeks every year at the end of October the town became 'en-fête' and this little place in Ireland's south-east corner was a Mecca for opera lovers from all over the world.

My earliest memories of this event are quite vivid for I was lucky enough to be living in High Street, two doors away from the Theatre Royal where the opera performances took place, and so on hand to witness the nightly excitement that went on in our street.

The first indication that something extraordinary was about to happen was when local electrician, Mr. Willis, would enter the street with one of his staff, a couple of ladders and yards of wiring to which were attached coloured bulbs. The street's decorative fairy lights had arrived. They were strung out in zigzag fashion from the corner of Rowe Street to the entrance of the theatre, and for twelve days or so our street was the best lit one in town.

For me and other children my age, the two biggest attractions of this event were the fireworks and the Guinness Clock. We watched one for minutes and the other for hours! Looking back, the fireworks were modest compared to the displays witnessed in recent years. The earlier mentioned rocket would be accompanied by perhaps a dozen more and that was it.

But the Guinness Clock – now that was something else! I remember standing awe-struck in front of it literally for hours outside the railway station, patiently waiting for the minute hand to reach the quarter-hour mark and see the little figures emerge from every corner of it. Included here was The Mad Hatter with his fishing-line, the policeman with his bell, the stork in the chimney, and not forgetting the Guinness toucans dancing around their tree. It was magical.

Other highlights included the shop window displays and the Opera Train. My two favourite windows were always those of Kelly's Bakery and Frank O'Connor's Bakery. I loved looking at all the amazing things shaped with bread in the former, and the large cakes of Wexford Bridge and Tuskar Rock lighthouse – complete with lights – in the latter.

The arrival of the Opera Train was also cause of great excitement to a ten year-old. This special train, its diesel locomotive bedecked with flags and bunting, carried the opera-going patrons from Dublin and was met at the station by some of the local bands which then escorted them to the Theatre Royal.

Back in High Street more of my boyhood memories include sitting in our darkened parlour with my sister, grandmother and uncle peeping through the curtains at the finery of the ladies and gentlemen passing our house on their way to the opera, and of the queues for tickets for the public dress rehearsals stretching all the way down the street around the corner into Rowe Street.

It was a long time for people to be waiting, and often as a result we would have our tea standing at our kitchen-table, owing to the fact that Granny had given all our chairs out to the people in the queue. Most of our neighbours did likewise and umbrellas were also supplied when the weather demanded.

Then in 1967 came a day that changed my life forever. Along with three other boys I made my Wexford festival stage debut as a page-boy in Rossini's 'Otello'. I can still vividly recall standing backstage in the darkness listening to the strains of the overture. The smell of the greasepaint in my nostrils, I was entranced by the feel of the fabric of my costume and then the heat from the many spotlights trained on the stage as the curtain opened and we made our entrance during the opening scene of Act 1. It was all so spectacular.

Now, almost fifty years on from that day, I have been lucky enough to have taken part in this great event as a volunteer backstage worker, chorister and currently as a front-of-house usher. I have made many friends and accumulated some wonderful memories, but those recollections from the halcyon days of childhood will always remain the most alluring.

Kevin Lewis, the music lover and artist from Clonard, Wexford town, was a prize-winner in the Ireland's Own Anthology of Winning Short Stories *in 2015.*

The Art of Love

By Thomas Martin

When we, as their maturing children, asked our parents about the early stages of their romance, they always denied the suggestion of love at first sight, but insisted it was their discovery of common interests that drew them together …

MY PARENTS were devoted to one another, and when my mother passed away my father fell into a deep well of loneliness from which he never truly emerged, during the few years left to him. This loneliness caused him to speak of her frequently, telling myself, my brothers and my sisters all about their life together, any time we had a family gathering.

And as we all lived more or less locally, there were many comings and goings, so he always had an audience. Talking about her was his way of keeping her memory fresh and none of us tired of hearing the stories.

He told us of how they had both earned their living working in the civil service and had met at a civil service dance (how traditional can you get?).

When we, as their maturing children, asked them about the early stages of their romance, they always denied the suggestion of love at first sight, but insisted it was their discovery of common interests that drew them together.

'It's important to have shared interests,' my father would say, 'but it's equally important to have your own thing.'

Throughout their courtship they enjoyed many pastimes together, including music sessions and set dancing and they were avid followers of the local GAA teams, football and hurling alike.

They also shared a passion for the cinema and went to see all the latest Hollywood and J Arthur Rank releases. My father enjoyed the Ealing Brothers comedies while my mother loved those big dramas Hollywood was so good at churning out. My father's favourite actors were Alec Guinness and Alistair Sim, while my mother's favourite was Clark Gable, whom she considered to be 'a real man', and Robert Taylor and Alan Ladd were also high in her estimation.

His favourite films were "The Lavender Hill Mob" and "The Ladykillers," while hers was "Gone With the Wind." She loved the sumptuous spectacle, the ball gowns, the melodrama of the historic storyline, the sweeping scenery of the Deep South. In later years, they would watch these films over and over again when they turned up on television.

But in all the time of their courtship – our father frequently told us – she had shown no interest in the visual arts. Then came the engagement, the wedding, the honeymoon and the settling in together.

Now in those days when a female civil servant got married, she had to leave that august profession to devote herself to the care of house and husband and, eventually, the children who would be the fruit of their union.

Such was the culture of the time and our parents accepted it as the way things were and had to be.

However, our mother, being a woman of some degree of common sense and efficiency, found herself with a lot of free time on her hands.

Daytime television had not been introduced and, although she liked a good book, she couldn't sit still for too long at a time. She liked to be active. So she decided to take up a hobby – something new, something different, something she had never done before.

As it happened, around this time, the local college ran an adult education course in art appreciation which included lessons in line drawing and an introduction to the basic techniques of water-based and oil-based painting skills.

She enrolled on the course and took to it with gusto, arriving home after the first lesson all smiles and flushed with excitement.

'Guess what?' she said to father, 'the teacher is Nora O'Brien, the lady who does the flower arranging for the church every week. Who'd have thought she was an artist – let alone an art teacher? And I know some of the other ladies in the class, from seeing them around the town. And we all go for coffee in the canteen after the class and have a natter. So I'm learning a new skill and expanding my social life at the same time. Good, isn't it?'

'Very good,' my father replied, 'but is it all women in the class?'

'Yes – there are no men.'

'And is that a good thing?'

'Oh, I think so.'

'I think so too, if what I've heard about those artistic types is true.'

Her first lesson was an exercise in line drawing, and her homework was to draw a sketch of a household object. She chose a can of beans – shades of Andy Warhol!

But it was during the second term of the course, having experimented with landscapes and still life projects (bowls of fruit, and so on), that she discovered what was to become her true love – portrait painting. 'Nora says that a well-executed portrait shows the inner essence of the subject – his soul, if you will.'

'People,' she went on, 'are what interests me. I want to paint portraits of real people, interesting people.'

But after a few attempts of painting portraits of a few local characters, she went off on a tangent and decided that the most interesting people she knew of were the stars of the silver screen; and certain stars in particular. 'I want to be a portrait painter,' she declared one day. 'I want to go to Hollywood and paint the stars, while there are still enough of them left. Real men are dying out. I want to capture the essence of their souls.'

'I thought they had treatments for that,' my father would say, in his light-hearted way. They were always bantering. They had the same arguments again and again, it was like a pantomime.

'You're a philistine,' my mother would say to him. 'Why didn't I marry a real man? A Clark Gable, an Alan Ladd, a Robert Taylor.'

'Alan Ladd is a shrimp. All the other actors have to stand in trenches when he's on screen.'

'You're just jealous. You haven't got his charisma.'

'I haven't got his money, either. I bet you can buy a lot of charisma if you have enough money.'

'Don't be ridiculous. Look at this younger generation of actors. James … what's his name – Darren?. Troy Donohue. Little boys, that's all they are.'

'Troy Donohue is six foot two.'

'I'm speaking about character.'

'And Clark Gable was Hitler's favourite character.'

'What does that prove?'

'I don't know, but it's an unfortunate association.'

This type of banter went on all the time. It was a kind of game they played and I believe her artistic pretensions were a technique for keeping it going.

But the one thing my father would never do was to criticise her efforts at portraiture, despite the fact, as he often told us – when mother was out of earshot – that she wasn't a very good artist.

Her aspiration to visit Hollywood was but a fantasy, but she began collecting cinema posters and movie stills which the local cinema owner let her have after each new film had exhausted its run. She used these as models for her paintings.

However, none of her portraits remotely resembled their subject matter. Every time she saw one of her heroes in a new movie, she'd have to attempt another likeness, but her Clark Gable looked like Sean Lemass, her Alan Ladd looked like Stan Laurel and her Robert Taylor looked like Dracula, with its exaggerated widow's peak. If she had only thought to rename them she might have been on to something.

'Why don't you do a likeness of Marilyn Monroe?' my father asked her one day.

'Don't talk to me about that one,' my mother said, 'she's a hussy.'

'Not at all, she's well read – there's a well-known photograph of her reading Joyce's 'Ulysses' on a film set, while she was waiting to be called.'

'Don't be so naïve. That photo was staged for publicity purposes. You don't think she was actually reading the book?'

'She's friends with the Kennedys.'

'Of course she is. They're politicians; they always cultivate associations with well known people. It lends them credibility with the public.'

'You're very cynical.'

'I'm an artist, I'm sensitive to the subtle nuances of human relationships. It's a gift.' But my father was only teasing her. The truth was he was more enamoured by the charms of Doris Day, the quintessential girl next door, pretty and unthreatening. A Marilyn Monroe would have eaten him for breakfast, not that he would ever be that lucky.

Every so often he would risk the dangerous question: 'so why did you marry me?' This was always followed by a long, pregnant pause. Then her tone of voice changed, modulating to a softer key: 'I saw something in you, don't ask me what.' This usually ended the conversation for a while. Sometimes, if the timing was right, they would send me off to the cinema for the afternoon. And nine months later, I'd have another sibling.

Sadly, by the end of the 1960s, all of my mother's idols had passed away, and all of them in their fifties. It seemed to be the fashion, back then, as Errol Flynn also died around this time, also in his fifties. All of these deaths were drug- or-alcohol related, sometimes both, although my father never mentioned this aspect of the film stars' lives to my mother.

'It's important for people to cherish their fantasies,' he told me from time to time, although I was a little too young to understand. 'It would be cruel to disillusion them. She enjoys the movies, and what harm is there in that? I do too, although plot development interests me more than admiring how actors look on the screen.'

After the last of her heroes passed away and the last of their films had been released and shown in the local cinema, my mother lost interest in the portrait painting. And the trips to the cinema became less frequent as by then they had a proliferation of television stations to watch. My father reached retirement age and they settled down to the contentment of their golden years.

My father took to gardening as a way of passing the time, 'a hobby most practical,' as Hercule Poirot might say. Both our parents had a fondness for the mystery stories of Agatha Christie; my father liked Poirot while my mother preferred Miss Marple.

My mother passed away in the late seventies, my father a few years later. Some time afterwards, when the house was being emptied out prior to auction, a remarkable discovery was found in the spacious attic, access to which had always been denied to us as children.

There amongst the usual detritus of a household – the lino and carpet offcuts, the unused wallpaper, ancient toys and schoolbooks, old LPs, a damaged button accordion, and umpteen boxes of I know not what – were thirty signed and dated portraits of my father, one for each year of their marriage. And here's the thing – the portraits were all perfect likenesses of my father, as he had aged throughout those thirty years.

And I know what my mother would have said if questioned about this: she would say that you can only capture the soul of a person if you know them very well. Those actors were only images on a screen but my father – he was the real thing.

Thomas Martin is from Clondalkin, Dublin. This is his first time to be published in the Ireland's Own Anthology of Winning Short Stories.

The Stick of Rock

By Eileen Casey

It was the glorious summer of Horslips, Mungo Gerry, shiny hot pants and sticky rock, and a tourist season spent with a friend working in a Newry souvenir shop – sheer heaven!

IT WAS THE summer of Horslips, Mungo Gerry, shiny hot pants and sticky rock. I was sixteen years old and working in a souvenir shop in Newry, County Down. The shop was owned by the aunt and uncle of my friend, Kate, and so, because of that close familial connection, my parents decided it was okay for me to go there for the summer months.

We got a lift up north from Kate's dad and we would be working nine to five or two until ten. On our free evenings we roamed the beach and generally hung out around the town. We loved the musicality of the northern accent, our own sounding much flatter than normal.

At that time, in the 1970s, Mary Quant, the dress and make-up designer, had a label called *Biba*, which was very popular in London's Carnaby Street. Our older sisters worked in England, training as nurses and shopped, when they could afford it, at the Biba Boutique.

Older sisters were great for parcels and kept their younger siblings in style. The craze for boys at that time was black plastic jackets which made them look teddy boy 'cool'. Plastic beatle wigs also found their way into our street and teenage boys wore them without any inhibitions, fancying themselves as pop stars and singing all the Beetle hits such as 'Love me Do' and 'She Loves Me, Yeah, Yeah.'

Kate and I got a pair of hot pants in the post from our sisters and we wore them on the beach, running into the water and enjoying the sensation of the foamy waves against our bare legs. As we came from the Midlands, we were more used to boggy landscape; here we had the mountains of Mourne and the sea. We gloried in the vast expanse of water glistening like a big bolt of lurex unfurled beneath blue skies. The undulating waves were endlessly fascinating.

The souvenir shop sold everything from plastic sunglasses, buckets and spades, hula hoops, mammoth size ice-cream cones to jars of bulls-eyes and clove drops. An entire shelf was devoted to glistening jars of rock candy. The rock was striped red and white or green and white, just like a barber's pole. Going down the centre, nearly an inch apart, were large letters spelling out NEWRY.

Stock for the shop was kept in a cupboard under the stairs and some nights when the 'goo' was on us, we craved the sugary bounty contained in cardboard boxes in that same cupboard. We took turns to creep down the stairs, holding our breath so as not to wake our sleeping employers. One of the steps had a 'strain' on it and if a foot landed inadvertently on this step, the creaking sounded like the opening of a Hammer House of Horror movie. The rock would be smuggled back and chewed and crunched until the 'wee' hours.

Years later, Kate and I came to the conclusion that her aunt and uncle knew about the nocturnal pilfering and probably wrote it off as a fair exchange for two bright shop assistants who were not averse to a bit of blarney with customers, young men to be precise.

They were an elderly couple with no children and they seemed to enjoy having us stay with them. We were popular, borne out by the fact that the tinkling bell over the door of the shop was seldom silent when we two were behind the counter. We were always punctual and gave no trouble. We were 'harmless' really, as the expression goes.

It was cosy under the eaves of that bedroom above the shop. The rock disappeared in quick time, the letters of NEWRY inching down like a melting candle. Sometimes, if we were particularly drowsy from the sea air, we might only get as far as NEW before sleep overtook us, our lips nearly glued from the sticky sweetness.

The other letters would be polished off as we got ready for work. We never left any evidence behind us, that's for sure. The peppermint flavoured was the most popular and by the end of summer, we had gone through a fair amount of it. So much so that while Kate still looked like a greyhound, I had piled on the pounds and could not get into my hotpants. My mother, a seamstress, had to let out the school uniform she made for me. I reckoned it was worth it though and to this day I still have a soft spot for sticky rock.

Eileen Casey is from Old Bawn, Dublin. This is her second time in a row to be published in the Ireland's Own Anthology of Winning Short Stories.

Echoes of Time

By Muireann MacGrafraidh

*It was almost tangible this rhythm that came from this cul-de-sac
of thirty two houses. It was the rhythm of life and the answering
resonance of people who lived in close proximity to each other,
a miniscule cosmos, a collage of life …*

THERE WAS A PULSE that beat hard and strong, a rhythm that echoed and eddied into the yellow and grey bricked street where I grew up. It was not the choked roar of the diesel trucks and buses that coughed black smoke on their way to the nearby docks and far flung suburbs. It was not the rat-a-tat of trains as they thundered at right angles by us.

It was almost tangible this rhythm that came from this cul-de-sac of thirty two houses. It was the rhythm of life and the answering resonance of people who lived in close proximity to each other. A miniscule cosmos, a collage of life, of loss and gain, of win and lose and oh … the colour, the mixture, the excitement.

It was an avenue by rights, by rights of Dublin Corporation who in its ever erratic wisdom christened us thus, although those cracked pavements were neither tree lined or wide. There were no front gardens, just two lines of double-gabled terraced houses that meandered drunkenly from front to back for they were rickety and well over a hundred years old.

'The houses that Jack built,' my Mother would say. It seemed to her as though the plans had got mixed up with a Georgian town house plan instead of artisan type dwellings. The hall door gave way to a long hallway. From this lofty vestibule were two large well-proportioned rooms with equally lofty plaster worked ceilings. The builders must have then discovered their blunder because the rest of the house was dark and pokey.

We had a yard and a garden of some forty feet that grew and held everything, anything and nothing. We all lived together in our crooked little house, my parents, my four brothers and myself, a cat, a budgie and a dog. The houses are now called 'Split Dormers' by estate agents. Back then you couldn't give them away they were in such disrepair. We were unaware back then of the coming attraction of our street being a tax incentive. As children we had our own idea of wealth; it was measured against what we knew.

The woman next door was rich and I knew this for a fact. It was obvious. It came down to scrubbing boards. Hers was not your plain, faded-out, washed–out coffee coloured, corrugated scrubbing board. Hers had a strong floral patterned corrugated glass inset surrounded by wood and her tin bath was white enamelled with a navy stripe that ran around the edge. It glinted and gleamed, it was very smart, unlike our dull grey metal bath that set my teeth on edge. I often stood fascinated and watched through the fence when on hot summer days she washed outdoors in the sun filled yard, the bath on wooden chairs, and scrubbed the clothes clean.

There were two apple trees in her garden and one stood on the edge of the concreted yard. There she stood in the dappled shade of the apple tree surrounded by laundry; it was almost a prayer tree. The sun gave her red hair a hue of burnished gold as her strong freckled arms and hands slapped the clothes onto the board. Her industry would grow into a sustained rhythm, a carbolic tattoo, and as she pounded and beat the clothes clean she sang. Hers was not a great voice but it had a wonderful melodic quality of its own; Dublineze sean-nos would be more accurate.

She sang songs like 'The West's Awake', 'Kevin Barry' and 'James Connolly'. Slow, haunting tunes were sung as her strong fingers gripped the clothes and slowly she pushed and pulled the garments up and down the board. She would rub the red carbolic soap well in as the rhythm of her hands increased and so did the songs until she was flying and the clothes were flying and roundly bashed clean to the resounding finale of 'Come Out Ye Black 'n' Tans' and ended with a final splash into another bath of water to rinse the clothes. As she sang and washed, apple blossom fell around her like soft pink rain.

Although we were surrounded by the hustle and bustle of life, death was also a part of that life. Granny lived two houses up from us and along with her friend, Fitzer, the one who sang songs of Kevin Barry and James Connolly, were the ones on the street who laid out the neighbours who died at home. Fitzer was short and plump with red hair and rosy cheeks. Granny was older, skinnier, had white hair and a pasty complexion; both were small in stature.

They were steely patriots and had first-hand knowledge of those years when we fought for ourselves, then among ourselves to sing our own anthem and fly our own flag. They, like thousands of women of their time, had seen and taken part and remembered those days that the rest of us only know from history books. I sat enthralled as they talked of old times - the hilarious and sad times, but mostly it was hard times.

There was a ritual to laying out a corpse; it was a serious business. They waited for three hours before they laid a hand on the deceased, for it was during these vital three hours that the departed was being judged.

'They are standing before their Maker and may He have mercy on them,' said Granny with thin lipped finality.

I had read Charles Dickens's 'A Christmas Carol' and shades of Jacob Marley rose up in my mind, and Ebenezer Scrooge on his knees begging for another chance from the 'Spirit of Christmas Yet to Come'. I pictured God as the God of Michael Angelo on the Sistine Chapel, powerful with a mane of white hair and a beard and eyes that bored deep into your heart and soul, and a finger that pointed you out and a voice that rocked the world.

I did have a nagging doubt, however, for it seemed to me that for a God who created the world in seven days, three hours was a long time to spend on one dead body. It only took ten minutes for the judges in the Irish Dancing Feis (festival) that I had danced in to reach a decision.

Suddenly Granny wasn't around anymore and Aunt Rosaleen cried all the days and never had a cigarette out of her hand. The world had suddenly become a cold, hard, alien place, as cold as the wind that blasted the crooked gables and the skewed chimneys that belched out black smoke; as hard as the steel grey sky that pitched down from above. Both houses were dark and hushed except for incoherent whispers and heavy sobs and coal being shovelled repeatedly onto dying embers. The radio was turned off, the television unplugged. I was bewildered until a cousin told me someone had died.

Aunt Rosaleen had come home for lunch and discovered Granny slumped on the floor in front of the range. Granny had suffered a brain haemorrhage and died. One moment she was laughing and calling to a neighbour, then closed the hall-door and went back inside the house, the house that had held her as a bride, a mother of seven, a widow and a grandmother – and after all that she had died alone on the cold scabbed slate floor.

Forgotten and unseen I stood in a corner and listened and watched. Aunt Rosaleen looked old, her skin was yellowed paper and she was dressed from head to foot in black. I noticed her hands, they were never easy and when she sat down, her long bony fingers pulled and plucked and twisted the threads and buttons on her black jumper and tugged at her skirt. Occasionally they curled into a tight fist that pulled the skin into polished ivory; then suddenly they would uncurl only to snap shut into a fist again. She was a black muted rage; her hands were never still.

There were people in the hall, on the staircase, on the landing. There were people downstairs in the kitchen, some were silent, some conversed in whispered tones. There were people in overcoats, women in hats, women in scarves, men with bared heads stood and others knelt on one knee and held damp drenched hats and caps as they answered the lone monotone voice that recited the prayers.

I inched my way along on my knees. I didn't want to be with strangers, I wanted to be with my family. The big back downstairs sitting room for some reason was the nucleus of all that was going on. I slipped in between the heavy dark coated forms that smelled of cigarette smoke and rain. I gazed at the floor as I went from darkness into twilight and found myself beside a polished pine coffin placed on wooden trestles. I stretched my neck and stood on tippy-toes to get a look. There, cocooned in satin folds, was Granny, her old hands folded and clasped, her white hair brushed about her in a candy flossed halo.

'Granny was dead!' I had never seen a dead person before, I was only seven. Startled, I looked about at all the sad faces and thought the only one that looked well was Granny. It was the first time in my life that I had ever seen her that she was not dressed in black. For this grand occasion I felt that she should have worn her soft black hat with the silver Tara brooch that sat on the side of her head and usually held in place with a vicious hat pin. She looked different, lost even, without her hat.

I reached out a hand and touched her pale forehead; she was cold. There was a sharp intake of breath from an older cousin who poked me in the back and rebuked me sharply with a 'Don't do that again!' I stared at her in scorn.

'…bye Granny…' I whispered. I looked around me, it was evening and dank darkness had descended outside. A low watt bulb that hung from a twisted electrical cord threw an obscure light into the room. On a bamboo bedside table two white candles stood each side of a black crucifix that normally stood on the mantle over the fireplace. The candles flickered and guttered and threw manic shadows against the faded floral wallpaper.

I watched the grey damp November mist steal into the room through the gap at the top of the sash window. Softly, stealthily it slinked into the room and enveloped the bare bulb until the dim light became a dull orange that scarcely if at all penetrated the blackness of the room. It was similar to the light an old bulb threw out just

180

before it blew. It is a sickly light that then expires with a soft hiss of a crackled element and dies.

I sensed an emptiness, a nothingness. Something that had been part of us had left and it, the room, all of us present, had changed. Our reality had changed. Granny had gone, Granny had left us.

Granny was buried in Glasnevin Cemetery beside Granddad on that November day. The day was a wet cold miserable one. We stood around the open grave as the prayers were said and as the rain poured down on top of us. As the coffin was lowered, Fitzer sang 'Danny Boy,' Granny's favourite song. The melody soared and bounced off the trees and the monuments, off the gravestones and off the great round tower and the square watch towers until the last note echoed, faded and died.

Muireann MacGrafraidh from Athboy, Co. Meath. This is her second time to be published in the Ireland's Own Anthology of Winning Short Stories. *She was published also in 2014.*

My Brother at Blackrock Baths

By Catherine McCarthy

Remembering a beloved brother who loved life and lived it to the full, before dying too soon. He was called Beamish by everyone after a TV advert for the Cork-brewed beer.

M Y BROTHER'S given name was Thomas Brendan but, as is often the case with children given the same name as a parent, he was called Brendan. That was until his friends gave him the nickname 'Beamish' when the advert for the Cork -brewed stout featured the slogan 'Sound man, Brendan' – everyone, including the family, quickly adopted Beamish as his name.

Brendan arrived on 5th August 1950, hot on the heels of our eldest brother and more than a month premature. They wouldn't tell our mother what weight he was for fear of frightening her, but my grandmother took our dad aside and told him to prepare for the likelihood that his second son would not survive.

Well, Brendan must have heard! Surviving and thriving, despite the lack of incubators in those days, was the first of a lifetime of challenges to which he rose magnificently!

Well, if he was in a hurry into this world, sadly it seems he was in a hurry out. Beamish was found dead in Thailand on 16th July. 2015, just two weeks before his 65th birthday. He had not been ill and an autopsy revealed nothing more than that he had died because he had stopped breathing and his heart had stopped beating.

His ashes were flown back to his son and daughter in New Zealand to where he had emigrated during the 1980s recession when they were 8 and 6 years old.

My sister and I travelled to Auckland for our brother's Memorial Service. This was a sad and emotional occasion, but more than that, it was a happy celebration of a full to bursting life, spent pushing boundaries, breaking moulds and refusing to conform or accept the constraints that society, convention or others tried to impose on him.

He was willing to try anything and did – a fruit-only diet, transcendental meditation, mountain climbing, public speaking, any kind of sport. Whatever his interest of the time was it would receive 110% of his enthusiasm and energy!

I brought home to Ireland a little phial of his ashes. Some I scattered on our parents' grave in Shanganagh Cemetery in Dublin, but most I brought to the place which came immediately to my mind – the place which to me epitomises my brother's love of life, courage and wonderful sense of daring, adventure and freedom.

I stood at the edge of the now sand filled 6-foot pool of the old Blackrock Baths – on the corner where used to tower the high diving platform. How clearly I can still picture him, as a young teenager, making his way up to the highest level – 'the roof' as it was called – and approaching the edge, seemingly without fear or hesitation. I was the one with my heart in my mouth!

When he looked down and then moved back, no one was surprised as that was most people's reaction! But in a moment he reappeared – this time walking on his hands, with his legs bent over his head for balance. He proceeded right to the edge, paused briefly and then kicked his legs into the air and somersaulted down into the water.

That was the memory I had in my mind as I released his ashes and his spirit into the fresh sea breeze at what remains of Blackrock Baths.

Go bhfaighe a anam agus anamacha na bhfíréan suaimhneas síorí. Amen.

Catherine McCarthy is from Shankill, Dublin. This is her first time to be published in the Ireland's Own Anthology of Winning Short Stories.